PETALS
IN THE GUTTER

SUSAN DELANEY

Published in 2024
by ©Susan Delaney

Paperback Edition
ISBN: 978-1-913898-84-7

Cover and Book interior Design by Russell Holden
www.pixeltweakspublications.com

Pixel Tweaks Publications
SELF PUBLISHING MADE SIMPLE

To all the young women who were placed in institutions for being unmarried and pregnant; and unjustly stigmatised and castigated as 'wayward' or promiscuous; or berated for being unable to repel the advances of men, this book is dedicated to you.

INTRODUCTION

It's astonishing how, in recent years, advancements in technology and mass communication have given rise to huge changes in social attitudes and behaviours. The issue of sex, for instance, and sexual behaviour, is more prominent in the public sphere than it has ever been. Seeing naked bodies, glimpsing openly sexual images and sexually-provocative behaviour has become normalised.

But it wasn't so very long ago, in the nineteen-sixties, that young people had scant knowledge of sex. Unlike today, there was no sex education in schools, and many parents found it difficult to discuss with their children crucial, personal information that would benefit them in their development and preparation for adulthood.

Growing up in the nineteen-fifties and sixties, many girls weren't forewarned of the decades of monthly bleeds to come, for example. Further, sex was a mysterious, forbidden fruit, reserved only for the sanctity of marriage. That, or something we might stumble across as a result of fumbling interplay between the sexes or, worse, a traumatic experience tantamount to assault, long before we realised that sex could actually be pleasurable.

For someone such as I, who felt compelled to leave home at seventeen to escape a domineering, dictatorial father who imposed harsh rules; and having grown up in a family of girls, and educated at a formal school for girls, my naivety, loneliness and vulnerability was a sure recipe for impending disaster.

And so my story begins when, aged eighteen, pregnant, and with no-one to tell, I followed my boyfriend to London, and immediately became homeless, and had to sleep on the streets. Pregnancy out of wedlock, and homelessness, were socially and morally condemned, and I had to try to hide both.

Seeking shelter, I was placed in a number of bleak institutions, and put to work. A series of blistering set-backs, rejections and injustices followed, including a struggle to keep my own baby.

Along the way, I met many wonderful women in similarly dire situations, and we developed strong bonds of friendship which gave rise to sisterhood and great camaraderie; and shared secrets and experiences that bound us together. My journey included moments of hilarious revelations, and bitter-sweet experiences like no other.

This is my story.

Susan

CHAPTER 1

'Miss. Miss! Are you alright? Can you hear me? …..Miss!'

The voices were urgent and rang around my head. I opened my eyes to find two Metropolitan Policemen towering over me. Feeling heavy and exhausted, I put my feet down to the ground and sat upright from where I had been lying on the bench. The reality of the situation hit me. I looked down to check that my suitcase was still there.

I remained sitting, fearful that if I were to stand up it may give rise to even greater cause for concern.

'Yes. Thank you officer. I'm absolutely fine,' I blurted, smoothing my untidy hair and trying to appear composed.

'Are you sure?' one of them said, clearly not buying my reassurances.

They must have thought that I looked extremely vulnerable. If only they knew how desperate I felt. I was eighteen years old and looked younger. A smartly dressed young woman lying asleep on a bench in the front entrance to St. Pancras railway station in London would have been regarded as slightly suspicious. This was long before the explosion of homelessness and rough sleeping.

'No, thank you, I'm fine' I repeated. 'I'm waiting for my boyfriend. He'll be back shortly. He's just gone to get some food before we set off.'

The second officer persisted: 'Where are you going?'

'We're on our way to Kilburn to stay at his sister's. She's expecting us very soon,' I lied.

That seemed to clinch it. Definitely a plausible response, I thought. Whatever doubts they may have had privately, my explanation was nonetheless acknowledged.

'Okay. Just so long as you're *sure* you're alright?' The first officer stared me in the eye, searching for more. I didn't falter. My performance merited an Oscar, or so I thought. He paused. 'Take care then, Miss,' he said. Thankfully, both of them moved onwards.

I breathed an inward sigh of relief. Sean would have gone mad if he had returned at that point. I would be letting the side down; a liability; holding him back. Giving him problems, that's what he would think.

The officers' questioning had attracted the attention of some passers by. Most of them started to move away, either to or from the railway station. Only one onlooker remained. He took a final drag of his cigarette, stamped it out, and slowly walked towards me. He had a pleasant, middle-aged face.

'That's my cab,' he said, thumbing backwards towards the London taxi cab parked nearby. 'Are you really okay?' Before I had time to muster another line of defence he continued: 'Look, my wife's at home. You can stay at ours for a few days if you want. You look like you're in need of a bed to me. There's a spare room; it's yours while you find your feet.' He paused, before adding in his broad London accent 'Straight up,' indicating that there would be no strings attached.

He looked genuine enough, but, despite his assurances, I was wary of any ulterior motives he may have had, and whether he really did have a wife at home. Besides, Sean will be coming back soon with some breakfast, and then we'll find a room somewhere, I thought. I thanked him, and told him that my boyfriend's sister must be worried that we had not yet arrived.

He nodded, conceding. On reflection, it really did seem as if his offer was authentic, and at that moment I would have loved nothing more than to accept someone's kindness; any sanctuary with a warm bed seemed an irresistible prospect, especially in view of the events of the previous twenty four hours.

A besuited business man appeared carrying a briefcase and umbrella, enquiring about a ride to Old Holborn, and the driver opened his cab door and turned to smile at me before driving away.

'Good luck' he shouted, and I think it was heartfelt.

I sat, watching people scurrying towards their destinations. They weren't like us. We didn't know where we were going. There was no way we could stay at Sheena's, or Anya's, Sean's two sisters who lived in London. This time it was out of the question.

I had met them, along with their respective families, only eight months' before. On that occasion Sean and I were still entranced by each other. It was the era of Flower Power. The National Express Coach had driven past Hyde Park filled with hundreds of people who seemed happy and relaxed, all appearing to wear clothes with printed flowers on them, and sporting flowers in their hair. Some held banners with slogans colourfully emblazoned with the words 'Make Love, Not War'.

Only much later on did it occur to me that many of these self-professed, loving people were probably high on illegal substances.

A lot can happen in eight months. It was nineteen sixty-eight, and I was beginning to learn about some of the harsh realities of life; about duplicity, dishonesty and unscrupulousness in the raw.

Sitting on that bench at the station I reflected upon the events of the previous day. Naively, I wondered how a day which had begun with so much hope could possibly turn so disastrously wrong. I had been so short sighted, I realised. But I had nowhere to turn; no one to tell. I had agonised over the matter of what I should do. I knew that I could not tell my parents. There would be no support there. After all, my father's aggressive behaviour towards me was the very reason I had felt it necessary to leave home in the first place.

The day before, I had crept out of my sister's home at two thirty in the morning, leaving a note to tell Jean not to worry. Everything is alright, I penned, and I would be in contact very soon. In truth, my placatory remarks were founded upon pure optimism.

I caught an all-night bus into central Manchester where I met up with Sean, as arranged. He had told me previously that he had some contacts in Luton who would be able to put in a good word for him on several building sites. There was the chance of 'the start', as he put it. They had also apparently offered a room for a temporary stay, if required.

'I'm definitely going,' he'd said. 'Do you want to come with me? There's nothing here for me in Manchester. But it's all happening in Luton, these fellas said.'

If I didn't realise it before, I knew then that I wasn't enough for him to stay behind for. I had already seen signs of waywardness, of the rogue that I was beginning to know. But I felt desperate. I couldn't stay at Jean's forever. She didn't have an inkling. In fact, she and my parents all thought that I was still working at The Sun Alliance Insurance Company in the financial sector in Manchester.

The reality was that I had fallen from grace. I was working at a Fire Salvage shop on Oxford Road in central Manchester. I had felt compelled to tell the Supervisor the truth. After all, it would soon become apparent. I felt certain that she had taken pity on my plight. She said that I could be offered temporary work on the express condition that I wasn't to climb steps, reach for items on high shelves, or do anything at all that involved carrying heavy goods.

'Do you understand?' she concluded sternly. 'We employ you until your time comes, and then you leave.'

I nodded. 'Thank you Miss Baines, for giving me this opportunity,' I said quietly, grateful for the prospect of having any sort of income.

In the nineteen-sixties most workplaces were usually run along fairly strict lines. Timekeeping was important, as was attendance. If there were any employee rights, they were not in evidence. For instance, there was no such thing as a recognition of bullying, or unfair dismissal. Furthermore, Managers or Supervisors had very high standards. Chatting whilst on the job, for instance, was frowned upon as was any perceived laxity in performance.

At the Sun Alliance Insurance Company I had been doing well, and I had recently been offered a new role in the draughtsmen's department, copying technical drawings for purposes relating to Building Insurance. That is when my problems had begun. My frequent lateness due to recurring morning sickness had landed me in trouble.

I also realised that in this highly reputable national insurance business there would be no place for someone whose morals were now questionable, or so it would have been regarded. I reluctantly served notice to leave. Working in a Fire Salvage shop, respectability was much less of an issue.

As I waited for Sean my thoughts turned to our arrival in Luton the previous day. By the time we had arrived it was already mid afternoon. Our planned train connections had not gone smoothly. We wandered around for a while.

'Where do these men live?' I asked.

'I've forgotten,' he said, trying to mask his embarrassment. 'I had it on a bit of paper. I must have left it behind.'

'Oh, you're kidding!' I responded wearily. 'How could you do that?' Neither of us had much money and I knew that staying in a hotel wasn't an option.

He dismissed it, as if it was no big deal.

'Come on, let's go this way. I seem to recall that Paddy said it was a small estate leading on somewhere from this garage.'

My heart sank. I should have known better than to expect a concerted, organised effort, with addresses, telephone numbers, and names of actual contacts. My suitcase was becoming heavier for me to carry. Sean had a small rucksack and a coat over his arm, and after some minutes' walk he took hold of my case and offered to carry it for a while. He must have imagined that it would quicken my steps, but I was in no fit state to hurry. Not long afterwards he handed it back to me, dropping it hard at my feet.

'Jesus Christ. What have you got in there, for God's sake, the kitchen sink?'

The truth was, I had all of my worldly belongings in that suitcase. Everything, that is, that mattered to me. Apart from some good clothes, I had precious keepsakes, and a myriad of various items I thought I might need.

We eventually found the estate. It was a larger than anticipated Council development. All the houses looked the same, with tiny gardens to the rear. We wandered through the maze of streets.

He said that he was hoping that one of the street names would sound familiar to the one written on the scrap of paper he had left behind. I was flagging. It was getting dark and I needed to rest, and to eat. I was five months into my pregnancy, and I was finding it hard to keep going.

We came into a narrow walkway flanked by gardens on both sides. Sean was becoming impatient. I sensed that he was realising the impossibility of his search. It had proved futile. There were hedges bordering the bottom end of some of the gardens. Looking demoralised he suddenly turned towards me and pushed me against a laurel hedge.

'Come on, Sue,' he said, running his hands down my front. Taken aback by his incredulous intimation, I pushed him away, thinking that maybe this was some sort of inappropriate joke. I regained my balance. Within another split second he pushed me back again into the hedge, and I knew that he was serious. I suddenly felt sickened.

'*No,*' I uttered wearily. 'Please, Sean, no. I'm *so* tired. Not *here.*' I pushed him away again but he was in no mood to stop. How could he even begin to think like this, I objected, but he continued, making it quite clear what he wanted. My protestations, and any attempts to dissuade him were in vain. He knew that I was unable to escape his roughshod demands. Where did this come from? I thought. Was this some sort of sadistic attempt to take out his frustrations on me? The suitcase was torn from my hand, landing with a thud on the stones.

'Shhh, *don't* make a noise,' he threatened. 'You'll have people coming out here to see what's going on. And if that happens, I'm running out of here.'

He forced my legs apart. His burgeoning physical presence bore down against me. I had no fight in me. Aggressively he pulled at my underwear. I turned my head, trying to look away, wanting this nightmare to go away. But it didn't. I was being violated, out here, just yards from people's homes. I was trembling, feeling more distraught than ever. My legs were going to give way, or so I feared.

When he had finished, he straightened his clothes and turned to make his way out of the passageway. Soiled, and unsteady, I tried to gather myself together, but my hands were shaking and I couldn't think clearly any more. Picking up the suitcase slowly, I trailed after him, choking back my anguished sobs.

'Come on. Let's go to London,' he announced, without a trace of remorse, as he came to the main road again. He either didn't care about what he had done, or he refused to acknowledge the abuse and distress which he had inflicted upon me.

I silently followed. What else could I do.

I had no choice.

The man who had professed his love for me not so very long before, who had written beautiful love letters to me, was someone I now hardly recognised. He was callous. I had been subjected to his brutality. He had chosen to ignore my wishes. He had treated me like a worthless piece of rubbish; a commodity to use when he sought fit, and then cast aside. There could be no love there at all now, on either side.

Sitting on the bench at St. Pancras Railway Station I found myself mulling through these events, and other fraught experiences which had occurred during recent months. Although I could not possibly have known then, they would all leave a lasting imprint on my life, and shape my future path. Right at this moment, though, I deliberated upon how quickly my circumstances had deteriorated into this abysmal state of affairs.

This was not just about one human being treating another despicably. The problem seemed to me to be much bigger than that. As a young woman who was unmarried and pregnant I had become instantly marginalised by society; I was deemed, in some circles, to be degenerate and worthy of condemnation, even abuse. I felt like a pariah.

A further flashback came to mind as I waited for Sean, that of another significant, disconcerting experience. Only three weeks' previously, I had been attending an antenatal appointment at St. Mary's hospital in Manchester. In the middle of my uterine examination the plummily-spoken male Consultant Gynaecologist turned to the young male student standing next to him and said:

'Remember, we are not here to judge the morals of this girl, but to provide a pre-natal service just as we would to a married woman.'

I was shocked. That statement spoke a thousand words. It was clear that he had *already* judged me. He was discharging what I felt were his misogynistic biases to the next generation of health providers. He had espoused the views that many people held at that time. That I was deserving of contempt. I was judged to be promiscuous, the term frequently bandied around in this new era of sexual awakening.

The fact of the matter was, that I had only had one intimate partner, the very same who had forced himself upon me against my wishes, who took my virginity. *What about the morals of the father,* I wanted to shout. But then, in this health environment I was not in a position to protest; I felt psychologically disempowered. I was in receipt of a service for which I was meant to feel grateful. More significantly I was in a state of intimate undress. I lay before them feeling bereft of any dignity, and humiliated. The Consultant had seen fit to render me not only morally inferior, but worthless. Moreover, he had chosen to do so as if I did not exist.

Like most young women of my generation I had resolved to be a virgin when I married. This was generally considered to be expected of a 'good girl'. To be respectably married before having sexual relations was the intention of most young women at that time. The same did not apply to young men. There was a double standard in which it was considered 'natural' for a man to want to 'try it on'. I had repeatedly resisted all attempts from Sean to get what seemed uppermost on his mind until I could no longer keep up the fight. By today's legislative standards, because the act had been non-consensual, he would have been regarded as having committed an act of rape, just as this last one had been.

I wondered how many incidences occurred in which men cajoled and coerced women into sexual submission, leaving them to suffer serious consequences.

At St. Pancras' Station I was jolted from my morbid thoughts and recollections by the sight of Sean bounding back towards me looking agitated and out of breath.

'Here,' he said, thrusting an apple into my hand. 'It's all I could get.'

'You didn't see any cherries?' Even as I spoke I realised how ludicrous my request must have sounded. Only a woman who has experienced hormonal food cravings during pregnancy could ever understand.

'No. And I could only manage two of these,' he stressed again, now slightly amused by his own, daring audacity, as he described creeping behind a street barrow piled high with green apples and snatching two of them. 'The fella looked the other way for a second and the whole lot came down in a heap! I just kept running.'

Despite never having been particularly keen on apples I crunched into this one, hungry, and glad to have anything to eat. I had never knowingly stolen anything in my life, or been party to a theft, but I was hardly in a position to disapprove of his actions. Who was I to berate anyone at a time like this. Any self respect, or lofty ideals I may have had came crashing around my feet months ago. My self-esteem was at an all time low. Simply trying to survive this surreal, precarious day-to-day existence was all that I could hope for.

'We need to hold on to what little money we have now,' he warned, just in case I might have had any unreasonable ideas about wanting some breakfast.

Sean was a fit, attractive young man, twelve months older than me. He was proud of his physical prowess. Not that he was muscular in appearance, but there was no doubt about his strength and agility. He had told me all about his skills in playing handball back home in Kilkenny. I was unfamiliar with the sport. He described it as a game of strength; a fast, men's game which was played in a handball court, something that could be found in most towns in Ireland, and open to be used by anyone.

Men used their fists to hit a ball hard against a wall, trying to out-manoeuvre their opponents who had to hit it next, rather like a game of squash without racquets. Sean had explained that he was regarded as a skilled local player back home. I could easily imagine that he would be good.

In our happier days when we had walked through a local park early one Sunday morning I had laughed at his ability to turn continuous cartwheels in a straight line. He was dressed in a suit, his Sunday best, and the sight of him had made me giggle as he showed off his athleticism. He had been full of fun then, and I had loved him for that.

Now, though, all happiness between us seemed to have faded. Here we were with no jobs, no roof over our heads, and I was expecting our baby. I had also now seen a side of him that I was wary of. I had no idea what I was going to do.

Having secured our main belongings in a station locker we walked out of St. Pancras Railway Station and onwards into the throbbing metropolis.

Sean bought a newspaper and he scanned the Classified Section for Rooms to Let. The average cost of a month's rent for a room only, plus another month's deposit, was much more expensive than the sorts of rents we had both, respectively, been used to paying in Manchester. There, in the leafy suburb of Didsbury I had lived in a spacious bed-sit with my own facilities, in part of a large, attractive house for less than half of the cost of the price of a small room with shared facilities in London.

Sean said that if he could get just a few days' work, with the money we both had left, we could then at least rent a room in a house somewhere in London.

In the nighteen-sixties the building trade was booming. In cities there were considerable numbers of transient people trying to find casual work; a day here, or there, and there was always the hope that casual work might lead to something more permanent. Illegal work was rife, especially in the building trade where you could be hired on the spot any early morning where additional labour was required without having to produce National Insurance Cards, or any other documents. Any likely fit male could be taken on for the day and paid a 'going rate', cash in hand, at the end of the day.

Sites were run mainly by Irish gangs. The foreman was almost invariably Irish and there were many young men looking for work, some of whom intended to stay, some not. Money was frequently needed back home in their rural economy, for their struggling families. For many, the capital was regarded as a place of opportunity and where 'London streets are paved with gold', as told in the nineteenth century tale of Dick Whittington.

Sean looked fit and strong. He had a pleasing face, and he had learned the sort of jargon to win over any fellow countryman who had the authority to 'hire and fire', and who needed extra men.

'But what are the real chances of you actually *finding* work?' I asked him. He seemed certain that he could. Glancing around I was less confident. There were no towering cranes or obvious building developments in the immediate vicinity.

We agreed to spend money carefully on food only, and that I would stay in public buildings for short spells during the day. At least there, I would have access to a seat and to pubic conveniences while he explored the area for potential work.

On that first day in London I spent several hours in a large public library in Camden Town where I leafed through innumerable books. I even managed to find some armchairs where I could sit back comfortably, and as my eyes scanned the pages it took all my concentrated efforts to try to stay awake. Falling asleep might have aroused suspicion. Worse, I couldn't even concentrate on subject matter very much at all, for worrying about our impending fate and what was going to become of us.

My library foray did, however, allow me time to reflect upon the increasing certainty that I could never again rely upon Sean to consider my needs, let alone look out for me. Besides, after the way he had treated me in Luton, he had clearly lost all respect for me. I knew, deep down, that there could be no permanent future for us. He, of course, would manage all right, I imagined. He was able-bodied, self assured and brimming with energy; ready to take on the world.

I, on the other hand, was feeling increasingly incapacitated, encumbered, with my chances of being able to look after myself progressively restricted. Nature intended the female of the species to have a nest in which to bring her offspring into the world, a place of safety, with the provision of her basic needs being met. Gestation only works well if a support system is in place, I ruminated. And I had none.

For now, though, we were in this predicament together; after all, I reasoned to myself, he *was* the father of my unborn baby. Strangely enough, he did still seem to care about that. Sean was from a large Roman Catholic family, and kinship and family mattered to him. He had told me about all of his ten siblings and I could tell that he loved every one of them. It had been a tough upbringing. Even his schooling had been a difficult experience with children regularly beaten by 'The Brothers', at the Friary School where, it would seem, every minor transgression was met with the threat of violence.

I had always been an optimist; a proverbial follower of the same beliefs as those held by Mr Micawber, in Charles Dickens' novel, *David Copperfield*, that 'something will turn up'. I had to keep going and hope that something would.

Dejected, Sean came back without having secured any work; the sites that he *had* discovered each had its full quota of men for the day. Gradually, as the light began to fall that evening, the impetus shifted to that of finding a place where we could sleep for the night.

Away from the buzz of the high streets many areas fell silent, especially after people had finished work and gone home. We wandered around in the dusk, looking for somewhere we could rest. We came across what must have been a small private coach depot, with some of its coaches lined up in an adjacent road.

Sean slowly circled the second coach which was parked some distance away from a street lamp. I watched as he checked windows and doors, hoping to find an entry point into the vehicle. This was long before the installation of high-tech, digital locking systems and alarms. With a sudden smash at the top glass of the door he had made a sufficient hole in the shattered glass through which to snake his hand, and he released the handle of the door inside. Ushering me impatiently into the coach he urged:

'Get in quick.' I followed gingerly, climbing the steps behind him into the refuge of the coach. Ducking down inside the unlit vehicle we made for the middle section of seats. I didn't really think about the seriousness of what we were doing. Each of us occupied a double seat, either side of the aisle, and I was never more thankful for that moment when I could finally lie down and sink into restful slumber.

CHAPTER 2

Had it not been for Sean waking me up at daybreak I would still have been there when the driver arrived only to discover foul play.

Walking out into the fresh morning air, having slept for some hours, I felt an overwhelming stab of conscience. How very wrong it had been of us to have gained unsolicited entry to someone's vehicle in that manner. Truly, I thought, we had been guilty of wilful damage and misappropriation. I felt deeply ashamed at our having stooped that low, and I said as much to Sean.

'Ah, they can cope with it,' he shrugged. 'What's a pane of glass to them? Nothing. They'll have it fixed by mid-morning and be taking punters on a Magical Mystery Tour later on. I'll bet you. Look,' he went on, 'they have insurance to cover this sort of thing.'

I knew right from wrong. The virtue of honesty had been drummed into me from being a small child, at home, in school and in church. My older sister, Jean, and I would run up to the old Methodist Church at the top of our road on Sunday afternoons, where we would go to Sunday School, and I would sometimes return again for the six o' clock service. I loved the hymns. The coming together in song. Our family weren't Methodists, but Dad allowed us to go because this church was nearby, and also because it gave my parents some 'time for just the two of them'.

Apart from proselytising the curse of drink, the subject of hell fire and damnation figured largely in the Minister's oratory to try to keep members of the congregation in check, and in attendance. The fact that our ageing Choirmaster ran off with my lovely young Sunday School teacher, leaving his distraught wife to suffer quite loudly in the front pew every Sunday, was testament to the evils of the world and, in this instance, the temptations of the flesh.

I now had to set aside all guilty thoughts about the coach. A new day beckoned. Not a beautiful day to be savoured, alas, but one in which I had to try to stay positive and hopeful that we could somehow resolve the problem of our vagrancy.

Before Sean took himself off for his morning job search we stumbled across a Quaker Meeting House which looked set to open at nine thirty to the public. The large notice board at the gate welcomed all visitors to enjoy its peaceful garden and to enter its lounge for quiet contemplation. We agreed to meet there when he returned.

I continued to wander around the High Street for a while, taking in the sights of the early morning rush hour. It all seemed so normal in the midst of our own crisis. A young woman smiled at me as she lifted out tin vases of flowers to fill the stands outside the florist's shop where she worked. I smiled back, and looked at the blooms. They were so lovely.

'Two bunches for two shillings' she said, 'I bought my Mum two for her birthday last weekend. She loved them.'

'They are beautiful,' I replied. 'I'm a long way from home, *and* my Mum,' I added wistfully, but wanting to appear to be looking interested, and *normal*, I rejoined, 'I think I might buy some for the flat on my way home. What time do you close?'

'Six o' clock tonight', she answered cheerily.

'Okay, I'll see you later on,' I said.

Why do I waste my energies and efforts engaging in such unnecessary subterfuge? *Drivel!* I chided myself. But how I longed to have somewhere where I was expected to *be*, a place of work where I was known, and liked. Better still, a flat to call home. Somewhere I could lovingly place flowers, kick off my shoes and sit by the fire with a cup of tea. That would be heaven, I dreamed, as I moved on along the street, peering into shop windows where I could see people readying themselves for opening.

Heavy traffic sped by, sending wafts of noxious diesel fumes and flecks of dirt at passers-by who were oblivious to it, so hell bent on getting to work on time, they were. My pace was more of an amble, a trudge forwards, counting the minutes until I could return to the place of our intended rendezvous.

By the time I managed to get back to the Quaker Meeting House, I could see that the front door was open. Walking up the garden path I sensed a tranquility in the garden that surrounded the main building. Inside, there appeared to be no one at the reception area so I walked towards another door immediately to my left that was wedged open. It was a light-filled room with shelves of books, a few tables, and some chairs placed in a circle.

I was startled by the sudden appearance of a woman of around the age of fifty, plainly dressed, with her hair pulled back into an immaculate French Pleat.

'Good morning!' she greeted, 'An early bird. Have you come to attend the talk next door, or did you drop in just to find out a little about our beliefs?'

'Oh, good morning,' I replied, 'Yes, well, the latter, really,' I said. 'May I browse through the books and the information?'

'Indeed you may. As you can see, there's a kettle over there, with some tea and coffee. Feel free to make yourself a drink, and help yourself to any of the information. We cannot allow any of the books to leave the house, I'm afraid, but you can take as long as you need to read, or to contemplate.'

I thanked her, and moved towards the shelves in anticipation of finding a good reason to settle down into a comfortable chair.

'Please don't hesitate to ring the bell on the front desk if you have any questions you would like me to answer, and I'll do my very best to help.'

'That's very kind. Thank you,' I acknowledged.

As she turned to leave, I relaxed, letting out my middle. Holding my breath and reining in as much evidence as I could of my widening girth had become a reflex action. I was at pains to try not to draw attention to my pregnancy. I was aware that I looked younger than my eighteen years and my slim frame was beginning to reveal my secret.

I peered back through the open door to the hallway where the woman had placed a free-standing billboard, on which the words read:

'Free Talk. 10am-12pm: Finding Our Own Inner Peace.'

'That sounds interesting,' I thought, as I toyed with the idea of going next door.

Common sense quickly prevailed, and I came back to earth with a bump. I recalled a wonderful lesson given by my fifth form tutor, Miss Ireland, who reigned quietly confident in her lesbianism long before the advent of LBGTQ, and who was a darling of a woman. She introduced us to the theory of 'Maslow's Hierarchy of Needs.'

She explained that Maslow, who was an American psychologist, created a triangular model in which the most basic, and essential, human needs such as food, warmth, shelter and safety, formed the base of his model. Only once our basic needs were met, he argued, would we be able to advance higher, by engaging in other pursuits which met our needs of esteem, intellectual growth, aesthetic, aspirational desires and quest for fulfilment.

Right now, I reminded myself, as if I really did need *any* reminder, I had been recently relegated to the very lowest rung of Maslow's Hierarchy of Needs. In fact, I mused, my legs were probably dangling precariously from its bottom ledge, about to plunge into the great abyss. I decided that 'inner peace' could never be mine so long as I had nowhere to lay my head.

I watched as a small number of people trickled through the hallway and made for the next room. Yes, I speculated, they all *definitely* had more than their basic needs being met. What's more, these well-heeled, self-possessed looking individuals had probably already risen to the dizzy pinnacle of Maslow's hierarchy, I mused, and may even be in danger of losing their foothold from the very top.

I made a cup of tea and chose a seat facing the window. I glanced through a number of pamphlets which explained the history of the Quaker movement, and the basis of its beliefs.

A beautiful lilac bush, planted in the border outside the window, billowed its pink and purple blooms, scattering tiny petals against the pane of glass. For a few precious moments I *had* found some minutes of calm and beauty, distracting me from the inner turmoil that waged a war within me. Momentarily, I felt safe here: from the outside world, from Sean and from whatever else might befall me.

I stayed in the lounge for as long as I felt it looked feasible to do so, and a good while after the people next door had left.

The slight chill of the morning had given way to a beautiful sunny day and as I walked into the garden I looked to find somewhere to sit, and to eat the sandwich I had bought earlier. It was important to me that I wouldn't be seen to be 'killing time' or, worse still, appearing to have nowhere else to go.

The garden was mesmerising. It was a green haven of plants, shrubs, trees and wildlife, all, incredibly, set within a stone's throw of the busy road. Here, on a bench in this idyllic garden I had the opportunity to have a bite to eat, and also to try to think through my rapidly developing problems.

The issue of homelessness in the post war years represented only a very minor social concern compared with that of the growing numbers of homeless people in the twenty first century. Back then, it was much less visibly commonplace in towns and cities. Anyone daring to sit on a street corner and to beg, for example, would be quickly moved on by the police, and generally regarded dispassionately. Further, we still tended to regard people in the main who did not have an address as 'tramps', or vagabonds; they were people who were often considered to be 'social misfits' or non-conformists who didn't care to be housed. As a result, there were very few charitable, religious or social sector support agencies at that time, most of which have sprung up since then to help the growing numbers of homeless people, and those on the street needing not only offers of shelter but of sustenance; and to support those with mental health problems, drug and alcohol dependency, and similar problems.

Religious institutions were still influential in the nineteen sixties, as were social ideologies which underpinned what was viewed as the importance of marriage and the nuclear family, and their pivotal roles within society. This was also a period which preceded the advent of the Second Wave of feminism, and the later introduction of the Equality Act; a time when cohesion of the family depended upon restricted rights and opportunities for women who were only expected to go out to work until they married, or started a family. There were very few opportunities for women to rise substantially within the ranks of the workplace to compete with men, who were still viewed, by and large, as the main breadwinners, and thus able to earn a 'living wage'.

Conformity to expected social norms was a powerful determinant of behaviours, not just for women, but for men also, and whatever problems and injustices may have prevailed behind closed doors, whether it was hardship, violence, physical or emotional distress, usually remained precisely there, hidden away from view. For such problems to have been revealed would likely result not only in feelings of shame and outrage but invoke indications of perceived dysfunction and fear of harsh intervention. Fleeing from such a home brought its own set of social problems. Pregnancy out of wedlock was still widely regarded as shameful, and very often single, pregnant girls and young women were sent away to have their babies, who would then be adopted. This practice appeared to erase the problem; deleting it from the sphere of home life, but decades later we are now beginning to understand the legacy of psychological damage and years of distress which many of the mothers of those babies have suffered. Many babies were taken from new mothers by force, and many other women were told that it was for the best; that they must not put their own selfish needs first. Despite some growing concerns at the time we still lived in a more closed society in which familial and individual problems were concealed or suppressed.

In that peaceful Quaker garden I reflected upon the idea that, in a sense, *I* had unwittingly broken convention. I had given up my sixth form studies, and therefore also my early prospects of higher education, so that I could obtain work purely in order to leave home. I was seventeen years old, and I was desperate to escape the physical aggression and hostility levelled towards me in my teenage years by my father. The legal age of adulthood was twenty one. Furthermore, I quickly realised that in doing so, in my naivety and loneliness, I had become even more vulnerable, and I must have appeared to be 'easy prey' for any chancer who wanted to 'push his luck'.

I needed to be realistic now though, I thought, and try to deal with my present predicament in the very best way that I can. I was only too aware that I was morally and socially scorned by many who would learn of my difficulties. This therefore gave rise to deceit on my part, and concealment in relation to both my pregnancy and the fact that I had nowhere to live.

I decided that the best way forward should probably begin with our pretending that we had married very young. At least that would provide us with some sort of pseudo-respectability. I had no yearning whatsoever to actually marry Sean, but since my pregnancy was increasingly becoming obvious I decided that I would need a ring on my left hand, ostensibly to confirm a 'respectable' status.

It was time to move on from the Quaker garden. I feared that I might become too conspicuous from the Meeting House window as having spent most of the day in their beautiful spaces, and the last thing I wanted to do was to heighten any suspicion. As I made my way out through the large wrought iron gate, I suddenly caught sight of the figure of Sean fast approaching from a distance away. As he neared I could see that he was grinning from ear to ear, and clearly looking very pleased about something.

'Things are looking up,' he said, having caught up with me. There's a new housing estate being built not too far from here. The foreman, a man by the name of Kevin Mulrooney, said he has nothing now but he said to turn up at six o' clock next Monday morning and he may be able to take me on for a few days.'

'That's great,' I responded, trying to appear to be pleased and encouraging about his news. Privately, I had mixed feelings. That was five days' away. In the meantime my unborn baby was increasingly letting its presence be known, such were its movements. Perhaps he or she was trying to tell me to 'get my act' together; to get more rest, and to return to eating more nutritiously, as I had been doing in Manchester.

No chance of that yet, I thought.

I was becoming increasingly concerned about our situation. I was also feeling very tired. I had hoped that we would be able to have somewhere to stay, if only temporarily, much sooner than next week. I was facing the prospect of having nowhere to sleep for more nights than I dared to think about.

For now, though, as I explained to Sean, I thought it was necessary to see if I could buy a cheap ring for me to wear, anything at all that resembled a wedding ring.

I didn't have long to wait, for two hundred yards along the high street I set sight on a branch of Woolworths.

Fifteen triumphant minutes later I emerged from the local branch of Woolies, the familiar department store that everyone knew so well, that sold anything from clothes to bicycle clips, wearing a band on the fourth finger of my left hand. To all intents and purposes it looked like a real gold wedding ring, and only we knew that it was nothing but a cheap metal fake. Not bad for seven shillings and six pence! I thought.

My persona suddenly took a new turn. I now wore the badge of 'respectability', and I could suddenly breathe without having to hold huge intakes of air, *and* let out my beautiful bump, naturally. This baby had been loved from the moment I knew of its being, and would be loved forever, I was sure of it.

In addition, I felt it necessary to seal my sham status by using Sean's surname. Thus, in one magical purchase I became Susan Delaney, and left behind my real name of Linnell. The truth was, I neither welcomed the ring, nor the name change, but if we were to look like a real married couple in order to be deemed 'respectable', and thus acceptable, then that's what it takes; for now, at least, I thought.

We sauntered aimlessly along the busy high street, our feet propelling us forwards with no notion of where we were going. I caught sight of my reflection in one of the large shop windows and was abruptly reminded of how different I was beginning to look. With only access to public toilets, my usually fastidious daily personal hygiene and care of my teeth and hair had become impossible to sustain. We had no access to facilities where we could bathe or wash properly. These personal habits of a lifetime had become much less important in the scheme of things than the job of managing to survive on the streets, and needing to keep moving on; I was too busy worrying about where we could sleep for the night and trying to work out how we were supposed to get a foothold into some sort of normal existence. Ablutions and self care had, out of necessity, taken a back seat, and yet I was increasingly feeling uncomfortable and unhappy about it. I longed to get into a warm soapy bath.

Nagging doubts kept flitting in and out of my head: had I done the 'right thing', in agreeing to follow Sean in the first place? After all, he wasn't the most reliable person on the planet. On the other hand, how was I to have known that his supposed promise of work and a place to stay would not materialise? And what other choices did I have? The fact was, I conceded, I didn't have any other option. I had to take the risk that I did in accompanying Sean, and it had backfired. There was a price to be paid: being without a roof over our heads meant that we had to walk the capital's streets in the hope that a miracle would happen.

I had not managed to save any of my wages from my office work in Manchester. At one point I'd had three regular jobs in order to pay for my expenses, plus many of Sean's too. I'd been working at the Sun Alliance Insurance Company in central Manchester, full time from Monday to Friday, I had a Saturday sales job in Lewis's Department store near Piccadilly, *and* a clerical job working for three evenings a week in Cheetham Hill for Rothmans, the cigarette manufacturer. All to try to help out Sean, who was always short of money and in need of help to pay his rent, and to eat. What a fool I had been. So in love with him then, gullible and naive.

The great myth of the nineteen-sixties, that it was 'swinging', that everyone was 'having a ball' or at least a great time could not be further from the truth, as far as I was concerned. As in all decades, there were great changes, but the influence of the church and other powerful institutions within society resulted, as ever it did, in harsher penalties for females than for males who, for whatever reason, fell short of expected norms.

Now in Islington, as the day wore on our steps became slower and fewer, and we needed to find somewhere to sit down for a while.

We came across a small green enclave between a main road with its high street shops and that of a residential area through which shoppers and workers hastened on their way home. It was largely triangular in shape, with small areas of grass, lined with shrub-filled beds and some low box hedges and ornamental trees. There were a few benches, and some public toilets were situated at one end. We stopped to rest for a while, and stayed until the sun slowly set for the evening. Without speaking it, we knew that this had to be our resting place for the night. Fortunately for us, there was no sign of rain. After eating our main meal of a bag of chips, wrapped in newspaper from a nearby Fish and Chip shop, when all seemed quiet and late enough to do so, we lifted our feet on to our respective benches, and slept.

The next morning I awoke first to the sound of early birdsong, but mainly because I needed to go to the toilet. The urgent and more frequent need to urinate was of course due to the increased pressure on my bladder from the new life I was carrying.

When I returned to my park bench, still feeling crumpled and untidy, I could see from looking in a small hand mirror that my face bore the indentations of my shoulder bag and its long strap, which had served as a pillow for my head for the night. My sudden outburst of laughter woke Sean up. This face, upon which I had once carefully applied my sixties' Twiggy, and Jean Shrimpton-look makeup, ready for the office, now looked devoid of anything except deep, criss-crossed creases. I thought that I looked hilariously disfigured.

'Jesus Christ, are you losing your fucking marbles?' Sean garbled, as he half opened his eyes.

'Something like that,' I giggled. 'You could say I've mislaid my shooter,' I grinned, cryptically referring to the game of marbles and trying to inject a witticism into the start of the new day. I waited for a response, but it was lost on Sean who hadn't yet woken up properly, and was still busy rubbing his eyes and yawning.

'I'll find it though!' I added.

'What the hell are you going on about?'

'I'm starving' I said, getting up from the bench, as I tried to pull my hairbrush through my long, dishevelled hair. Today had to bring something better, I enthused.

This day, however, which began with a sprinkling of mirth and renewed sense of hope on my part, slowly, as the hours wore on, sank gradually deeper into what seemed like a great void of loss and displacement.

From the beginning, we had both agreed that it would be inadvisable for me to return to the same places where, on previous days, I had been able to while away the hours until

Sean returned from his early morning work search. More lengthy visits would look decidedly odd, we agreed, and therefore each day we traipsed onwards to a new area. Today's walk took us to a mixed area of low-rise blocks of flats contrasted with older, terraced properties in Islington. Although the main streets had a good selection of shops and services we weren't able to pinpoint a public library or any other, similar public building where I could stay for a few hours. Since we had no means of contacting each other we both agreed to meet up near a launderette, which stood between a newsagent's shop and a general store.

I loitered around the area, drifting up and down the roads which threaded between the residential blocks of dwellings. For a short time I waited at a bus stop where I could at least sit on one of the folded seats, pretending to wait for a bus, and then I peered through countless shop windows on two nearby, small shopping parades.

The newsagent's shop had almost half of its window covered with personal advertisements written on postcards, and I spent some minutes idly browsing through them all. Having read a card upon which a lady had written that she was looking for part time help in the house with her children and domestic chores, I had a brief delusory notion, thinking that maybe I could apply for the position. Until, that is, I soon realised the absurdity of such an idea, given that I had no fixed abode. How could I ever appear ready to undertake *any* job having slept on a park bench for the night, and with no change of clothing from one day to the next? More importantly, how could I ever turn up for work with a face that resembled a game of noughts and crosses?

Sean's search for casual work on a building site seemed much less likely to give rise to personal scrutiny of *his* attire, or whether or not he had happened to have had a wash and shave in a public toilet. Builders cared much less about whether a man had brushed his teeth that day, or that he was wearing the same pair of trousers he had worn the day before. Men's appearance in general was much less likely to be judged in the way that women's were.

I sat for a time watching mothers and their toddlers in a residential play park situated in a communal area between the blocks of flats. I found it hard to picture that this might be me in a couple of years' time. Those women had husbands who were out at work all day, I imagined, enabling them to care for their little ones and undertake their associated duties of housewife.

Single mothers of independent means did not seem to exist. Those rare few who managed to get by on their own did so either by living in their family home, or by going out to work all day having been offered nursery places or other forms of childcare to look after their offspring.

One thing appeared certain to me: that those mothers did not lack security. I imagined that they would soon be returning to their flats or houses, then perhaps preparing a mid day meal before putting their little ones down for an afternoon nap. There would be routine; there would be food in the larder, and shillings, however few in their purses. Later on in the day, although it was May time, they would be making a fire in the grate or switching on the heating for a while to ward away the chill of evening, before making their way to their cosy, respectable marital beds. I was idealising their circumstances, and I knew only too well that some of the mothers may not indeed live in quite such agreeable circumstances. However, I was beginning to feel disconsolate and dispossessed.

'No,' I resolved, inwardly. 'There's no place on the street for self pity. Longing, maybe, but there had to be a pragmatic way forward out of all of this.' I rose to make my way slowly back to the launderette.

As I strolled back, I dwelt upon other, difficult times I had experienced in my young life. My older sister Jean and I had had a much more strict upbringing than those of our peers at school. My younger sister Kay suffered less at the hands of my father who had softened his approach by the time that she came along. When Dad was in a good mood, though, and something disappointing happened he would jest, in mock encouragement:

'*Now remember*, your mother never bred a jibber!' to which we would all fall about with laughter. But the message was clear: 'pull yourself together and get on with it'.

The irony was, it was my *father* who ruled the roost, *and* with a rod of iron; my mother had very little influence on any major decision to be made in our lives. Dad was domineering, and sometimes extremely harsh, but if I were to mention just one saving grace I had gleaned from him it was my resilience in the face of adversity. Moreover, it was my *mother's* steadfast endurance of many years of the controlling, bullying behaviours of my father, that inculcated in me a capacity to withstand difficulties, and to try to move forward with as much fortitude as was possible. This particularly trying time that I *now* faced, I determined, would pass, and I knew that 'something would turn up'. You could call it blind faith.

Surprisingly, when I reached the launderette, I could see through the window that there were no customers doing their washing, and so I went inside and sat down for a while, waiting, as I had become used to doing, for Sean to return. Five minutes' later, two young women bustled through the door with their bags of laundry, and two trolleys, as we used to call pushchairs, with small children fastened inside. It was time to move on again since it was obvious that I had no laundry to be washed or dried, and I suddenly felt embarrassed that I was sitting in there at all.

Without having been able to stay in any one place in particular during the morning the time had weighed heavily upon me, and I was relieved when Sean turned up and we could move on together.

'No luck,' he chimed. 'Think my best bet is waiting until Monday morning when Mulrooney will hopefully take me on,' he said.

Quietly we trailed onwards, without an inkling of the direction of our wanderings. I only hoped that Sean would be able to remember how to find that new housing development again where he had been given to understand by Mr Mulrooney there might be the chance of work for him on Monday morning.

The afternoon ended once again with nothing to show for it. We were running out of money fast, and hope was no longer in abundance, as far as I was concerned. London can be a vast, lonely place when you're down on your luck.

The end of the day drew closer and we came to a very run-down residential area comprising row upon row of old, terraced houses. We walked up one of the streets which illustrated shocking examples of impoverishment and dereliction. The houses all appeared to be badly maintained, uncared-for dwellings with peeling, dirty paintwork and years of dirt on windows; many of the tiny, front gardens were also unkempt and strewn with bags of rubbish and discarded remnants of furniture. Some of the houses had sheets pinned across their front windows where curtains or blinds should hang, whilst other houses were boarded up. There were no vehicles parked in the street. I wondered if squatters were the only ones living up this street, or whether people actually paid for the privilege of living here.

Sean suddenly stopped.

'Wait here,' he said, and he pushed back an old wooden, full-sized gate which stood between two houses. It had come off its hinges and had been wedged shut.

Minutes later I heard his footsteps coming back, and he reappeared, beckoning me to follow him. As we proceeded into the alley he wedged the gate back in place again.

'Don't make a sound,' he warned, as we walked towards the back of one of the houses.

The alleyway gave way to a yard, and though it was getting dark I could see that it had been used as a repository for all manner of scattered detritus. There was a stench of sewage and decay. I wasn't sure if Sean had forced entry into the back of the house, and I didn't ask him. I was now beyond caring. It was obvious that the place wasn't occupied.

We made our way into the room which had once been the kitchen, and onwards into the long passage that was the hallway. The old Victorian floor tiles were still in evidence; a beautiful tessellated floor that women once diligently mopped and polished was just perceptible, now secreted under layers of dirt. We peered into the first living room we came to, and crept onwards to the second room which was located at the front of the house and overlooked the street beyond.

Although it was dark we could see that the walls were damp, and black mould had permeated its way from the corners of the front wall to surround the windows. Elsewhere in the room the remaining wallpaper was a reminder of the life that once lived there. The property looked as if it had been abandoned some years ago.

'We can sleep in here for the night,' Sean said, unrolling our two lightweight mackintoshes and spreading them out on the dirty linoleum floor in front of the hearth.

I felt dispirited, and resigned to the prospect. How had I come to plumb to *these* depths? I sighed heavily. How quickly my fate had turned, from being an independent young woman with a promising future ahead of me, to that of being practically penniless, sleeping in a filthy, derelict house, and expecting a child in just over three months' time.

This baby was an important part of my existence. Having a baby hadn't been part of my big plan, though. I hadn't intended to have intimate relations outside marriage in the first place, and contraception had not been available to me; but since this life *had* been conceived I accepted the fact that I had no choice, and then came to actually embrace the idea. Abortion was not yet legal at this time and, although I was aware of the availability of illegal abortion, taking those risks did not even enter my head: I had heard, and read, about some of the terrible consequences for women and their babies. Four months into my pregnancy, however, abortion became legal, but by that time I was in trouble 'too deep'. My life, my whole infrastructure was disintegrating. But above anything else, this unborn life was *mine*, a part of *me*, and she or he was *wanted*, whatever else happened.

As I lay down on the cold, hard floor, I tried to negotiate, with great care, which parts of me could manage to fit on to my mackintosh and which, reluctantly, had to touch the filthy linoleum. I was still wearing the same clothes that I wore when I left Manchester: A light coat, over a skirt with an elasticated waistband and a full over- blouse. Underwear in the nineteen-sixties was not designed for comfort. Women still wore nylon stockings held up with a suspender belt, holding four suspenders, the buttons of which frequently dug into your thighs. Lying on a hard floor was made all the more uncomfortable by my constricting clothes. Worse still, my legs, covered only by the fine texture of my 'nylons', as they were called, were having to make contact with the filthy floor, which I found revolting.

Ladies' tights were not worn until the nineteen seventies. And although some avant-garde women were beginning to wear trousers well before that time it is fair to say that northern, working classes generally did not welcome the idea of women wearing trousers throughout the nineteen-sixties. Views ranged from their not being very 'ladylike' to downright antagonism because of their association with masculine apparel and the freedom which they could potentially afford women. Further, the idea of women wearing trousers challenged the idea of male power. The saying: 'Who wears the trousers in your house?' was grounded in the premise that men held greater power and significance, and were 'in charge', and therefore women had no business wearing them.

These ideas were very much part of a northern, Manchester, working class ethic. My father would never have entertained the idea of his wife, or his daughters for that matter, wearing trousers. Furthermore, for decades afterwards, on a much wider scale, women who wore trousers were actively discouraged from wearing them at official functions such as an interview for a job, or to a wedding. They weren't considered to be 'appropriate' forms of attire.

I lay for a while staring at the ceiling, which had once been a beautifully ornate feature of the room.

My thoughts returned to the idea that my life was spinning out of control; my fear that I now had no control over anything. Only now, I reflected, was I beginning to understand, first hand, how a female's biology could render her vulnerable and disempowered.

I harked back to an incident that had taken place a few years' previously in relation to my own dear Mum's situation. My father had come home from work for his mid-day meal and, after we had eaten, I cleared the table and then excused myself so that I could go upstairs into my bedroom to revise a few final details in preparation for my afternoon's scheduled, Biology GCE 'O' Level examination. I needn't have bothered, because of what was to follow: it was by no mean coincidence that this examination was the only one that I would fail, something, of course, which I couldn't possibly have known at that moment, nor either of the furore that was about to play out.

From the moment I had climbed up to my top bunk bed and opened a large file of notes I could hear my father ranting disparagingly about me; shouting at my mother that she should not have allowed me to go to study, but instead she should have insisted that I wash up the family dishes; that she was too lenient or 'soft' with me, and made needless work for herself by not making use of my assistance to do the job. My father's angry voice became louder and louder as he reached the bottom of the stairs where he shouted up to me, in no uncertain terms, that I should go downstairs *at once* to wash 'the pots', as we called them.

I reached the kitchen in the midst of a vitriolic torrent of my father's verbal abuse. He bawled at me. I was lazy. I was inconsiderate. I was selfish and didn't give a thought to my mother.

Meekly I attempted to explain: 'But, Dad, I *do* always help her but, today, ….' He immediately silenced me with an even more vituperous rant. Suddenly, he grabbed hold of my hair and pinned my face to the kitchen wall. He continued to yell into my face only inches away, his face red and contorted with anger. Finally, he let go of me with a hard wrench which banged my head against the wall, before storming out of the back door to go back to work.

My hands were shaking as I reached for a tea towel and began to dry the pots that Mum had already washed and left on the draining board. With tears streaming down my face I supplicated for the first time ever:

'*Why*, Mum, *why* have you put up with this for so long? *Why*? Why have you not left him?' I realised that these words, borne out of distress, were unprecedented. I had never been so outspoken to her before, or even *mentioned* such things.

Her hands and arms were still deep in soap suds in the sink. She stared at the wall ahead for several seconds then threw both hands aloft. She turned towards me.

'Do you really think that it hasn't occurred to me?' she answered, in tones of despair. 'Don't you think that I've wanted to? That I've tried to work out, time and time again, what I could do? *How* I could do it?'

I was shocked. My face suddenly straightened and the tears stopped.

'Where would I go?' she asked.

'What would happen to you and Kay? What was I to do? *Leave you?*'

That was an earth shattering moment in my young life: learning that my mother had wanted to leave her marriage, but couldn't leave *us*. Moreover, at a time when divorce and separation were still considered by many to be shameful, my quiet, introverted mother had actually contemplated it. Practicalities had conspired to prohibit her. She had no financial means of her own and therefore no way of being able to rent a property. Women were not legally entitled to apply for a mortgage until after the passing of the nineteen seventy-five Sex Discrimination Act but that also would never have been an option. She had no friends of her own, all thanks to my father preventing her from having such a life, and in not allowing her to go out to work, which she had always wanted to do. She had no family to go to. Furthermore, there were no refuges then for women, or agencies to support people who were victims of abusive relationships. She had no choice but to go on enduring the soul-destroying consequences of living with a bully and trying, simply, to get on and make the best of things. It had pained me to learn that my good, kind, hard-working, self-sacrificing mother had been thwarted at every turn and prevented from having access to a life where she could live peaceably and where she could have free expression.

This was the fate for many thousands of women, for well beyond the middle of the twentieth century. Today, the matter of a female's biology, and in particular her child bearing capacity does not necessarily equate with dependency, entrapment or subjugation, but in nineteen sixties' Britain it was a very different picture.

Only later on in my life was I able to see how my mother had attempted to equip herself with skills which might enable her to develop some sort of autonomy. At one stage she had endeavoured to go to night school to learn to type but my father had strongly dissuaded her from doing so. He had questioned why she wanted to do that. What did she think she might be able to achieve by learning to type? What a waste of money that would be, he had insisted. He poured scorn on the whole idea, until she felt defeated, bullied into submission. He would not have agreed to her spending that money, and therefore it was out of the question.

The same thing happened when she began to raise the prospect of her learning to drive. He asserted that it simply wasn't necessary. He argued that *he* would take her wherever she wanted to go.

My father never disclosed his earnings, and it was he, of course, who managed the family's finances, and therefore my mother's very existence depended upon whatever he did or did not want her to do, and what only *he* was prepared to pay for. In essence, he made sure that she didn't broaden her skills set; that she was grounded in an impoverished world of home-working, sewing for a pittance each week. He made sure that she was unable to broaden her horizons and gain the confidence to start out on her own. He actively prevented her from entering the public workplace. My mother's married life was therefore given over to the domestic minutiae of keeping hearth and home together, scrimping to make ends meet, caring for our needs, and most importantly for those of my father's.

She never, ever complained. She never argued. She never wept. She never owned anything to speak of, save the most basic of clothes. She was an exceptionally well- read, intelligent woman, whose life was one of servitude and obedience to a man who would openly declare his love for her, whilst denying her any rights. Her achilles' heel was that she was quiet, unassertive and gentle by nature.

Lying on that floor in the decrepit house, though exhausted, I couldn't stop thinking about my mother's powerlessness, relating it also to *my* current dire predicament. When I left home I had counted myself as fortunate in managing to escape the abuse, the misery that Dad had been wreaking but, was I now a renewed casualty of the same patriarchal web? A society which castigated me for becoming pregnant, and which didn't allow me a dignified voice to ask for help. A life in which I was reduced to this? Inwardly, I railed at the whole injustice of which, it seemed to me, half the population was subordinated to that of the other.

With a jolt, and simultaneous, startling alarm we opened our eyes. I half gasped. There were noises coming from the room upstairs, directly above our heads. We froze, and said nothing; horrified, I listened to the sounds of people above, and their muffled exchange. There were people in the house!

'We'll be alright,' Sean whispered. 'They're probably squatters. Maybe drug addicts, who knows. But they'll know we're here. They'll have heard us,' he said, with much certainty.

'What if they come down?'

'Don't worry, I don't think they will, but if they do, I can handle them.'

And I knew that he could.

My need for sleep overtook my wish to stay vigilant, and I drifted into a murky twilight of rest.

A new day dawned. A few strands of light managed to filter through the gloomy panes of glass, laying bare our stark and dismal slum surroundings, for all that they were.

I needed to go to the toilet, and quickly, so we gathered together our few things hastily and made our way out of the squat and into the London street. With no bathing or dressing to do, the job of getting on with each new day was, out of necessity, simplified to a tee.

We found some public toilets and continued onwards with our journey, and as we did so we happened upon the spectacle of Smithfield Market. Its noisy trading activities had been underway for some hours by this time, and at five o' clock looked to be at the stage of packing up. Moving on again, we were surprised to find that our meanderings had brought us back to the West End shops, and with it, the realisation that we had probably walked many miles' full circle since arriving in the city some days ago.

The last thing I wanted was to be reminded that London was regarded as the capital of the fashion world. Mary Quant, Jean Muir, Ossie Clark were just some of the well known British designers of world-wide fashion at the time and their colourful, pop culture images filled the shops with new geometric designs and transformative clothing accessible to most young people.

It was impossible, however, for a young woman to walk along Oxford Street or Bond Street without gazing in awe at the latest fashion trends for which London had developed great acclaim. We veered away from the world of high street fashion, cutting through side streets with their grand Georgian exteriors, some of which were private houses and others, places of business. My eye caught sight of a large, ecclesiastical-type building on the other side of the road whose steps protruded outwards on to part of the pavement in its ascent to the main door. It looked bizarrely out of place amidst the exclusive heartland of this part of the city.

'Wait a minute,' I urged Sean, 'I'm just going to see what this is.'

Crossing over to where the full, grand facade of the building stood proud, I stopped to read its large notice board.

'The Religious of Mary Immaculate Sisters welcome young ladies who are studying in London to stay with them, protected by God's Love and Care.'

I stared at the imposing noticeboard, reading and re-reading its message. Would the Sisters of Mary Immaculate welcome *me*, for just a little while, I wondered? I wasn't studying, of course, but I supposed that such young women would need certain domestic services being provided to enable God to love them and look after them. Unless the Sisters of Mary Immaculate did *all* of God's work themselves? But wouldn't their long habits get in the way of their mop buckets? I wondered. And with all the prayer needing to be done surely kitchen pans are likely to boil over, without additional help?

I turned towards Sean and we walked back together into the busy throng of shoppers and tourists again. I was anxious to discuss its possibilities.

My mind went into overdrive. Maybe this would be the start of my way out of this mess. It would at least provide a roof over my head. Suddenly, other potential benefits flashed into my head. I might be able to eat nourishing food again. I could finally be able to bathe, to clean myself and start looking after my self again. That is, if they would accept me into their world. I didn't know what their world would entail, but it had to be better than the one I lived in now. I could offer my labour in return for full board. It might be restorative, and somehow, just maybe, enable me to rise above my powerlessness.

I explained to Sean my idea. He listened and said nothing. I continued:

'Sean, it would be better for me, and the baby, if I could sleep and eat here, if they would take me in. Meanwhile, you could hopefully start with Mulrooney on Monday. There must be a YMCA hostel in London? Then, when you've earned enough to get a room for us you could come back for me and I'll join you. I was suggesting, of course, that we part company, at least for now. Further, I was taking a gamble, because I had no idea whether he would ever come back for me, and I had no means of reaching him. I didn't even know if I *wanted* him to come back for me.

'Sure I can see that it would be the best thing for you, for a week or so, but what's the chances of them needing some help?'

'I don't know, but if I don't try, I'll never know. But, equally, I just don't know how long I can manage to go on like this, with the baby developing and me not eating enough, and not managing to sleep properly. I have no antenatal care either, no one to keep an eye on things. Where would I end up giving birth? I'm so worried about it. I want to try, for the sake of the baby. You do understand, don't you?'

'Sure I do,' he said, quietly, beginning to look despondent all of a sudden. Was he contrite, I wondered? Did he regret not having been kinder to me?

'Go on, now,' he gestured towards the Convent. 'If they do let you stay, come back out to let me know, won't you?'

'I'll see you in a few minutes.' With that, I started back again towards the Convent.

'Good luck,' he shouted after me.

Before reaching for the door I hesitated for a moment, trying to gather my courage. I knew that I didn't look in great shape.

I didn't feel clean or tidy and I was conscious of it. My confidence had also taken a bashing, and especially so since I had left Manchester.

I took in a deep breath. 'Dear God, please take care of me and my baby,' I whispered. 'Please take me in.'

CHAPTER 3

The door of the large nineteenth century building was open, and inside was a small vestibule and a second, more decorous, opaque door with a crucifixion etched into its glass. I pushed it tentatively, and it revealed a magnificent hallway. I could hear somewhere in the distance the hum of collective voices, doors closing, and activity of sorts. There appeared to be no-one about on the ground floor. I felt like an interloper, hardly daring to walk further into its hallowed hallway. There was a beautiful staircase ahead, at the top of which were some striking stained glass windows with biblical depictions of the Virgin Mary, and in the central panel stood Jesus Christ, presiding over his followers. Around the hallway itself were paintings and iconography which would instil a sense of sobriety and reverence into the most earnest of believers. To me, straight off the streets, it was a moment of awe and humility.

I took a few short steps towards a door on the right so that I could read its sign more clearly: The Office of Mother Superior. Knowing little of Roman Catholicism and even less about orders of nuns and their religious life I supposed that the title signified seniority. Fortuitously, before I had time to knock on the door a young nun appeared from a nearby passage and asked if she could help me.

'Oh, thank you. Yes, I ….,' I faltered, 'I'm hoping to speak to someone in charge who might be able to advise me about something rather personal.'

'Now, let me see,' she paused, 'I think that Mother Superior may still be in prayer of the Divine Office, but I'll just check for you.' She gave a gentle knock on the office door with the back of her hand. A voice inside signalled her to enter.

Mother Superior had in fact returned from prayer and seconds later her tall figure appeared at the door. She invited me to step inside.

'How can I help you? Do sit down,' she said, indicating which seat she wanted me to occupy. I couldn't recall ever having had a conversation with a nun before. She had an air of confidence that I thought perhaps came with the habit, just like a knight who wore chain mail. I felt lowly and inferior; a small, northern soul of no importance who had somehow become adrift.

'Thank you.' I paused. 'It's very good of you to see me,' I said, still trying to compose myself. I felt like a fish having been scooped from the sea, gasping to try to survive. 'It's a bit difficult to explain,' I began. I was searching for some sort of inspiration to know how best to find the most appropriate words. This was all the more challenging knowing that some of them would have to be downright lies.

Mother Superior sat a short distance away from me, her presence looking every bit a figure of authority. She looked piercingly into my eyes.

I began again: 'My husband and I recently travelled from Manchester, mistakenly thinking that we had a place to stay and that a job was on the cards for my husband. Unfortunately, it all fell through and,' I looked downwards, then, remembering a phrase that I'd read in The Lady magazine: 'unfortunately we're now in reduced circumstances. The fact is, also, I'm five months' pregnant,' I said, surprising myself because it was only the second time I had said this to *anyone*, the first being to the supervisor of the fire salvage shop in Manchester where I was hoping to be offered a job, and felt compelled to disclose the fact. I was in an even more desperate situation now, and there was so much more riding on it.

My Woolies' ring glistened on my finger, looking every bit the 'real McCoy', but I was careful not to make it too obvious, as if I was deliberately trying to prove a point. I continued:

'My husband has been offered a new job, starting next Monday, and he will be staying in a YMCA hostel until he can earn enough money to rent a room for us. It will only be for a short while, but I wondered if you might kindly consider utilising my skills looking after the young ladies, and allow me to stay here for a while?'

She continued to stare at me intently. She glanced down at my ring, but almost disbelieving of it she said:

'Where in Manchester did you get married?'

'The Holy Name,' tripped off my tongue. It was the only Roman Catholic church that sprang instantly to mind. One which Sean and I had walked past on Oxford Road in Manchester on our way towards the boarding house in Rusholme where he had once stayed.

I tried to hide my panic, suddenly hoping she wouldn't ask me the name of the priest who married us. That really would be getting in too deep, I thought, having to think up a third whopper of a lie.

'Wait here a moment,' she instructed. And as she rose her long black attire spun before me, rosary beads tinkling from her waist, and she whirled out of the room in seconds. I waited, tense with apprehension and anxiety. I could hear muffled voices from within the hall. When she reappeared she brought in the young nun I had met earlier, and whom I later came to learn was a postulant, or novice. 'Follow Sister Cecilia and she will tell you what you need to know.' The young woman hastened, and I had just enough time to thank Mother Superior and to express my gratitude before she turned her attention to other matters lying in front of her on the desk, and also before Sister Cecilia herself disappeared.

The young nun led me up two flights of the elaborate main staircase, then leftwards through a series of passageways and several doors. A final door opened and I was led into a large dormitory which was divided into rows of cubicles. The sight was slightly reminiscent of the formation of back-to-back terraced houses with alleyways between each row. Walking down the first row on our left hand side, she opened the door to number five and led me into the tiny space within.

'This will be your room while you're here. There's a toilet just through the door at the far end. When you've taken off your coat, you can leave your bag here and come and find me again on the ground floor and I'll take you to the dining room where you can start to serve lunch.'

'Thank you Sister,' I said, hardly able to comprehend what was happening.

I heard her footsteps disappear through the door and out of earshot.

Sitting on the edge of that narrow bed, I tried to take it all in. I breathed out great sighs of relief. It was as if I had been enacting a role where spontaneity was called for. I could almost hear the applause.

Dad always used to say that I had a vivid imagination, and I knew that that was true. This was the era of Ken Loach, the screenwriter and director, with his new, natural approach to acting on screen. I used to enjoy the few drama lessons we had at school with the gym mistress in which she tried to get us to use our bodies to act out a part. On one occasion she called for volunteers from the class to enact the behaviour of a beatnik, a 'cool dude' of the sixties. Several girls in my form looked round at me and called out for me to do it.

'Bet little Sue can do it. Come on, Sue,' they urged. I was a shy teenager, but in this role no speech was called for. I nervously stepped forward and, on queue, strutted my stuff, swinging imaginary beads as I sashayed along, chewing imaginary gum, clicking my fingers to the non-existent beat of a pop song, and looking anti-establishment and 'devil-may-care'. I received instant cheers and claps of approval. Though she was smiling, I knew that I had surprised the mistress, because I revealed a side of me that was quite unlike the quiet, obedient, dutiful no-hoper of a gymnast or athlete that *she* knew. I was able to shift into a completely 'different gear', into a new environment, and pretend to be another person.

The actress in me came to my rescue at a time like this.

The cubicle was spartan, with just a single bed, a small table and a chair. By far the most imposing feature of the enclosure was a fireplace, over which was placed a ceramic figurine of Jesus Christ. Much higher up, under the picture rail, hung a large cross that must have been visible from inside every one of the cubicles.

I assumed that the privileged, fee-paying, international students slept in rather more attractive accommodation than this dormitory but, as far as I was concerned, I had a tiny, heaven-sent space which I couldn't have appreciated more than at this very moment.

I was still clutching my shoulder bag in my hand as I gazed around at my new refuge. I felt an overwhelming sense of relief in that this new setting, austere as it was, far outstripped that of the derelict house, the park bench or the various seats and benches on which I had been resigned to having to sleep for the past week. The tension that I felt in having had to rise to such a challenging situation, now dripped from every pore, and I felt emotionally 'spent'. A tear splashed on to the leather strap of my bag and I quickly stood up to shake myself out of shedding more. I felt grateful for the sanctuary; for safety, for usefulness, for finding a place to belong, however long or short that was going to be. I wiped my damp cheeks, closed the door of my cubicle and proceeded to make my way back to the street where I knew that Sean would be waiting.

The sunshine of the day looked more beautiful than it had done only a short while earlier and my smile must have indicated to Sean what he needed to know.

'So, you're in, then?' he said, taking my hand.

'I am. It's a good thing,' I beamed. 'I am so pleased.' I was careful not to appear to be ecstatic because I was aware that he would probably still have to be roughing it for a few days' longer. 'There's work waiting for me, Sean, so I'll have to make this brief. I want to show willing and give them as much help as I can.' I reached into my pocket and handed him my tiny locker key. 'I want to ask you a big favour: will you please go back to St. Pancras' railway station and get my suitcase, and bring it here for me? You could just pop it inside and tell one of the nuns that it belongs to me?'

He pulled me close to him and pecked my lips.

'You take care of our baby,' he said. 'I will miss ye, you know, Sue.'

In that instant I felt overcome with sadness for him, for us, and for what we used to have together. There were so many contra-dictions. How could he miss me, when he had been prepared to go it alone initially, despite 'his baby'; and he had hardly been loving or caring since we left Manchester. He had actually been a brute towards me when we were in Luton, something that I would never forget. After that we had simply co-existed on the streets; we had shared the same misery of homelessness.

'Look,' I interjected, 'find out where the nearest YMCA is. I'm sure that the money you have left can run to a few nights' stay at the hostel until you start work on the building site and earn some more.'

'Don't you be worrying about me, Sue. I'll be alright. I'll come back for you when I have a room for us. Okay?'

I nodded, but I felt torn about what I really felt and what was best for me and the baby. At the top of the steps I turned to wave briefly, but he was already striding back towards the busy main thoroughfare.

I have to make a go of this, I thought. I have no time to waste.

I don't know how I managed to spur into action after the events of the last week, but the adrenalin, and the need to be seen to be earning my keep, kick-started a new raison d'etre within me.

Ten minutes' later I was being handed a blue tabard which I placed over my head, and fastened, with press studs at each side of my middle. Another member of staff, a rather odd-looking, squat, young woman muttered:

'Up here,' and she took me into a serving area at one end of a large dining room.

'When they come in just ask 'em what they want,' she said, and promptly walked back to the kitchen.

That comprised my induction to the job.

I stood behind the serving counter, along which large basins of hot food had been set into a long, stainless steel, heated unit: mashed potatoes, roast potatoes, carrots, peas and cauliflower, roast lamb, sausages, and a large stainless steel jug of gravy. I lined up the oversized utensils and glanced at the day's menu behind me, just in case anything might be missing, though quite whom I would tell I wouldn't have known.

I expected that another member of staff might be joining me, but as the students slowly began to trickle into the dining room I soon began to realise that the serving of the meal was all down to me. I was 'on'.

I smiled at these women who were barely a few years' my senior, in fact some must have been eighteen, like me. I later learned that the nuns accommodated international female students between the ages of eighteen to twenty seven years old.

'Hello,' I said, looking at two young women who appeared at the counter first, followed quickly by more. 'What would you like?' Each student collected a tray and, glancing at the menu or directly at the cooked food on offer, stated her choices. I found myself responding diligently to each request, working my way along the counter according to their wishes. No one had mentioned anything about portion control: how many potatoes to put on each plate, how big the size of each spoon of vegetables should be, or how much gravy to pour over the ingredients and so I relied upon my instinct. There was no time to find someone to ask, and apart from anything I wanted to appear to be competent and someone who used initiative.

Like all young women of my time and class I had, of course, served many meals to members of my family. Most young working class girls were brought up learning how to prepare, cook and serve meals. On the rare occasions when our extended family visited our home we would offer greater choice by placing the food in dishes on the table so that they could be passed around for people to help themselves but, in general, my mother would spoon out the food straight from the pans or dishes whilst in the kitchen, and hand me each plate, telling me:

'This is Dad's,' or 'this is Kay's,' and so forth. My mother always sought fit to make light work of the washing up, so we dispensed with serving dishes and reserved them only for times like Christmas, or Easter, when grandparents might visit. We were a family of girls, therefore we all learned these routines, without being taught but, just as with other domestic tasks, we watched our mother, and learned to do the same.

My mother told me on several occasions that, growing up alongside her brother, it was always *she* who had to serve meals and refreshments to her father and her brother. It became clear to me that she begrudged always having to serve her brother. She was expected to serve her brother *and* his friends when they came round to play games and, later on, as teenagers, when they all practised playing in their jazz band with their washboards and other make-shift instruments.

'Susan, our Bill never lifted a finger!' she would say. 'I was made to make refreshments for them, serve them, and fetch and carry for all of them,' she confided, discontentedly.

Shortly into the first course, the assistant who had provided me with the initial scant, 'savoir faire' came slithering into the serving area, carrying a lemon meringue pudding, followed by another dish of chocolate sponge pudding and, finally, a jug of custard sauce. I thanked her, but seemingly oblivious to my politeness, and lacking in any social graces, she said nothing and slithered off back again in silence.

Students gradually returned their trays with empty plates and cutlery to a sectioned rack, and those who wished to have pudding lined up for a second time. I was getting the hang of things now, and smiled some more at them, and even ventured to say a few times that I hoped that they would enjoy it. This was what good, working class girls did: learn to serve, and accommodate others' needs, with a smile.

51

As a young woman, this new role didn't stretch my resources too heavily other than, on this first occasion, the need to acquaint myself with the processes which supported the service, such as how and where to replenish the dishes which were depleted of foods, and how long the mealtime continued, for example. However, for someone who had not eaten a proper meal for over a week, being surrounded by the sights and smells of delicious-looking food, and feeling exceptionally hungry, this mid-day service tested every sinew of control that I had. I found myself wanting desperately to make a grab for some of the potatoes and push them into my mouth, but because I was conspicuous to all those individuals in the dining room I didn't dare to try. The temptation was almost unbearable, and I couldn't wait for the moment when they had all gone.

As the door closed behind the final departing student at the far end of the room I could bear it no longer. I sank a serving spoon into the leftover mashed potato and shovelled it quickly into my mouth. This was followed by another, and then some leftover carrots. Suddenly, the near door at the end of service section burst open and a nun wearing a full white apron strode towards the counter.

'How did you get on?' she asked briskly, as if she had already met me. She began lifting out of some of the dishes from the serving bench. I gulped down a final clump of cauliflower which, thankfully, she had just missed seeing me spooning into my mouth. Clearing my throat of all delicious fare I answered that I felt it had gone very well, and thanked her.

'Now, will you start to sweep the dining room, and also around this serving area? I'll get someone to clear all these dishes. You'll find a broom in that cupboard over there,' she said, pointing to the end of the area where a cupboard was secreted into the main wall. 'No need to mop until after the evening meal,' she added.

'Yes Sister, of course.' Mortified as I was to see the leftovers being removed out of arms reach, I wondered if any of the staff had the opportunity to eat the leftovers after each mealtime. I swept the dining room floor clear of any crumbs and debris, and returned the broom to the cupboard where it had been kept. After emptying a dustpan of its collected bits into a bin that I had discovered under the counter, I was making my way out of the dining room when a now-familiar voice said:

'Want some food?' The resident inmate poked her head around the kitchen door and invited me in. Did I want some food? Not half! But I tried to look only casually interested in the prospect, stifling what could easily have been a hysterical squeal of over-enthusiasm. I walked through the kitchen door to where a group of the staff had congregated around a table. Plates were slid noisily around to each person seated, rather like someone dealing cards, while another young woman, who was remarkably similar in looks and mannerisms to that of the first woman, and with the same limited communication skills, lifted some dishes and two pans into the middle of the table.

There were six of us, sitting around the table: the two lookalikes, a thin, late-middle-aged woman whom they called Minnie, an older, slightly hunched woman who wore her grey hair in a long thin plait, and another young woman who wore a permanent scowl. The nun in charge had already taken her leave, and I gathered that she had gone to prayer, after sharing a meal with the other Sisters.

We were a motley crew. Each of the five kitchen staff had the look of underprivilege or disadvantage. I sat down and waited. Minnie began to say grace, and so I reverently put my hands together and bowed my head, but she raced through it at such speed as to make it indecipherable and inconsequential. By the time she had reached the word 'grateful' the two squat women had spooned two helpings on to their plates and the meat had already reached their mouths. Had the nun-in-charge been present I was sure that we would still have had our eyes half shut.

Between us we scraped and polished off all the food that had been left over. We ate in silence. I made a pathetic attempt at small talk but no one seemed to want to engage in conversation. Heads bent over, there were only the sounds of slurping and the smacking of lips until the scowler went over to the ovens to see if there was any pudding left. There was some lemon meringue stuck to the inside of a large dish which two of them promptly attacked with knives and duly finished off, but I felt replete for the first time in ages, and so I began to clear away the remaining plates and dishes on the table.

'You can leave those there,' shouted Minnie, looking over towards me at the sink. 'Sister Keiran has very high standards. *We* have to see to that.'

I knew that she wasn't implying that I didn't have high standards, but probably that she knew exactly what to do and that I, the new girl, wouldn't know where to start; that the kitchen jobs were *their* responsibility, for which they felt a sense of ownership. Either that, or they didn't dare to want to risk the disapproval of Sister Keiran when she next entered the kitchen, in case the new girl hadn't done something quite right.

'Okay. Thank you,' I said. It fell on deaf ears, as they set to, silently demonstrating their domestic know-how of finishing the job of clearing away and washing the final items.

The older woman with the plait came up to me.

'What you did, *I* normally do,' she said, staring into my face and waiting for my reaction, her head strangely cocked to one side.

Unnervingly, I thought that she was expressing a grievance about the fact that she had been taken off the job of serving meals and deployed elsewhere, *because of me.*

'Oh my goodness, have I taken your job?'

'Nah, don't worry 'bout it. I'm glad of the change. Sister Keiran put me on peeling instead. I got to sit down.' She grinned, and scuffled out of the door, and for a brief moment I thought that I detected a limp in her gait, before she was gone.

Walking back up to my cubicle my head was racing with all that had happened. It was almost mid afternoon. I hoped to snatch a rest, but my new experiences were buzzing around my head.

I lay flat out on the single bed, staring at Jesus with his outstretched arms on the mantelpiece. A whole bed to myself! A full stomach! Were my fortunes beginning to change? In my heart I knew that this could only be an interlude, it would be temporary. This 'half way house' was only a mere stepping stone, but a very welcome one for now until I reached a more secure footing, I thought. This was a strange place. These events didn't seem part of real life, however grateful I felt for them. This microcosm of religious life and its inhabitants preoccupied my thoughts.

I hadn't met people quite like these members of staff before. From what I had gleaned they all lived in the convent and supported the nuns' mission of providing protection to 'Roman Catholic young ladies' from overseas who were in London to learn English. But to what extent were *they* in need of protection also? I wondered. All of them appeared to be quite vulnerable individuals themselves. I was left with the impression that some of them had lived here for a long time. No doubt I would find out a little more, but as I lay there I couldn't help but speculate on their lives, and what brought them here, to live and work under the supervision of the nuns.

All of this was incredible to me. The events of the last week seemed surreal. Only this very morning, I thought, I woke up on a dirty, cold floor of a derelict house, and here I am now, lying on a strange, albeit very welcome bed, having started a new job, and working with a group of people who appear to live in a parallel universe.

My eyelids felt heavy, and I was beginning to succumb to the tiredness that came with stress, bewilderment and the sheer exhaustion of it all.

'Susan, it's Sister Cecelia.' A light knock came tapping on the cubicle door.

I scrambled to my feet. When I opened the door the young nun was standing before me. I must have looked sleepy.

'Oh, hello Sister.'

'Did I tell you that the evening mealtime starts at seven o' clock?'

'Oh, no, but I thought it might be around that time. I'll be there, Sister.'

'Good. Now, don't forget, Susan, if there's anything you need to know, please feel free to come and ask, won't you?' she said as she was already beginning to walk away.

'Oh, and by the way, your husband dropped off your suitcase. I tucked it right in next to the stairs in the hallway, so you can bring it up whenever you're ready.'

Surprised by the speed at which Sean had retrieved my case from St Pancras railway station and walked back to the convent, I almost forgot to ask her about the next important thing now on my mind: where the staff bathroom was located. This lovely young nun stopped for a few seconds more to describe how to find it from the passageway leading from the hall.

Sister Cecelia appeared to have a sunny disposition. She had a warm, open countenance and she was full of youthful optimism, energy and happiness, unlike the other nuns I had already seen about the place. I found it hard to understand how someone 'brimming with so much life' would want to commit themselves to a relatively closed community for the rest of their lives.

Glancing at my watch I could see that I had only half an hour to go before I had to be back on duty, and so I decided to go and bring my case up to my cubicle before my work shift began.

The evening mealtime service ran along very similar lines as the earlier one, except that there were more students having supper than those who had eaten lunch at mid-day.

The food looked equally as mouth-watering as before, with the first course being slightly lighter: it was a choice between macaroni cheese and shepherd's pie, with optional vegetables of carrots and green beans. Pudding looked tantalisingly delicious: bakewell tart with custard sauce or fruit trifle with cream.

It occurred to me that most of these dishes had been made since I had left the kitchen. The staff had clearly been working almost continuously since their clear up after the mid-day meal. I began to think that, in my being asked merely to serve three meals a day to students, I was being let off lightly compared with the workload that the permanent, resident staff members undertook.

Agnes and Constance, the two portly sisters, along with Minnie also, had returned to the kitchen at three thirty, in order to prepare, from scratch, the dishes for supper, under Sister's direction. The scowler, and the older woman with the plait, whose name was Dorothy, joined them later to help out for two hours before supper; they had more time off mid afternoon because they undertook some cleaning duties every morning instead, assisting two daily non-resident members of staff who came to work for the Sisters each morning.

I found the students to be more relaxed than earlier in the day. They seemed to want to enjoy each other's company more, having finished their day's study. As a result, the supper service lasted a little while longer than the more brisk, mid-day service.

After all the students had left the dining room I helped the kitchen staff to carry the depleted dishes into the kitchen. I washed around the serving counter, then swept up and mopped out the whole room. It was just past eight forty five by the time I switched off the lights and closed the door behind me.

I felt very tired. The other staff must also have been feeling the same, and they still had a fair amount of work to finish off after we had eaten the leftovers. Once again, we all ate in silence, other than Aggie and Connie who burst into fits of giggles when Connie dropped half of her portion of macaroni cheese on the table. She blithely spooned it up and deposited it on her plate, and even scraped the table clear of the food, licking the spoon so as not to waste any of it. After we had eaten there wasn't a scrap of food left to put into the bins.

Tired as I was, I found myself observing every nuance of the behaviour of the staff. It was as if I was part of a kitchen-sink drama, with the players slowly revealing key aspects of themselves and their backgrounds, even when they weren't saying anything. Their mannerisms, their poor language skills and forms of communication, their body language, their manners, or lack of them, and their clothes and deportment captivated my imagination. There was much that I wanted to find out about them, but I wasn't able to. I found it all spellbinding, especially in view of their being resident in this unusual religious community of women.

I knew, from the very first encounters with these staff that they probably hadn't had the best of starts in life, and therefore their education had also been limited. It wasn't until the nineteen seventies, and in some cases well beyond, that individual educational needs, to a greater extent, were addressed. Often children slipped 'through the net' if, for example, they had hearing problems, learning difficulties, or other challenging problems. The introduction of Teaching Assistants who work with small groups of children, or on a one-to-one basis, in order to try to enable them to learn more effectively is a relatively new phenomenon. Before this, many children were alienated from an educational system which effectively failed them.

There were other indicators that these staff members had also had an upbringing which lacked good levels of communication and basic, nurturing care.

At that stage in my life I had only my own upbringing, and those of my peers as a yardstick against which to adduce others' behaviour, values and skills, but I was able to detect that Agnes and Connie, in particular, had what at that time was regarded as low levels of intelligence. This later came to be associated under the great 'umbrella term' of special needs. The other three also appeared to have difficulties of various sorts. Despite this, their collective productivity, under the supervision of Sister Keiran, seemed to me to be quite astonishing.

I was anxious to see if I would be able to have a much-awaited bath, and become clean and fresh again, after my week of living on the streets. I went down to discover where the bathroom was, hoping it would be free. I opened the door to a beautiful room which was quite unlike any bathroom I had seen. Its had dark brown tiles, edged with small decorative tiled motifs; a bath that was boxed in with a tiled front also, unlike our bath at home which had clawed feet. There was the most beautiful antique glass shade I had ever seen, set into the ceiling. Unlike my cubicle, I was able to lock this door and I was grateful for the privacy it afforded, whilst I sank into a very deep, warm bath. The sheer pleasure I felt, as I gently submerged my body into the water, was something that I would remember always. I have never been so grateful of warm water engulfing my whole body as I was on that evening. All the discomfort I had felt in my feet after walking so many miles ebbed away, and the sweat and strain on my body, slipped into the deep water as it gently lapped around my distended frame. I knew then that I would never again take the gift of water for granted.

In my tiny cubicle, after my first day in the convent, not only safe but clean also, I had the soundest of sleeps. It was heavenly.

In my suitcase I had packed a small travel alarm clock and I had set it for six o' clock. Breakfast had to be served at seven o' clock, and so I got up promptly the next day and slipped my coat around my nightdress to go down to the bathroom. Shortly afterwards I dressed into fresh clothing for the first time in over a week and made my way to the dining room. I felt refreshed, and much happier than I had, of late. I could smell the delicious cooking of an English breakfast from the first floor landing and knew that I had a job to do before I could look forward to any of the leftovers.

Porridge, cornflakes and fresh fruit were already set in the counter, ready for serving, along with vacuumed jugs of fresh coffee and stainless steel teapots full of tea. Aggie made her inimitable, ungainly entrance into the serving area holding a basin of rashers in one hand and fried eggs in another.

'Mushrooms and tomatoes comin' up,' she uttered, short and sweet.

'Thank you Aggie,' I said, watching her waddle back towards the door. She walked, as my father used to put it, at 'ten-to-two'.

Dad would regularly point out some poor soul's gait:

'You see him?' singling out some unfortunate victim whose feet pointed outwards as he walked, 'you don't want to end up like him! Straighten your feet!'

Smiles didn't come easily to these staff, but I felt happy again, and smiling was what I'd been brought up to do, so smile I did, at all these bright-looking young women.

They seemed to come from virtually across the globe. They were fresh-faced confident-looking young women, who wore an air of privilege. I heard Spanish, Italian, Chinese and French accents, as they chatted effusively to their friends and newly acquired acquaintances, and I picked out their requests and placed them neatly on their plates and dishes. I noted their tasteful clothes and accessories; beautiful slip-on shoes that I'd seen Audrey Hepburn wearing on billboards, and chic, expensively-cut hairstyles. They were good, middle class Catholic girls, excited to be in London and enjoying their first time away from home. Life must have seemed super-sweet to them, and I was here to serve them.

I was aware that Great Britain had always welcomed refugees fleeing persecution from their overseas homelands and also, more recently, we had seen an influx of people from the Caribbean who were welcomed to fill labour shortages. However, at that time Britain, in general, was not a multi-cultural society. Also, on the home front, most working class people didn't have a passport, and the arrival of cheap European travel was still to come. Therefore, mixing with, and talking to, 'foreign' people was a new and interesting experience for me, even if it was only limited to their choices of food.

I learned that the students were accommodated in two very large, exclusive residences a short distance away, and that there was a resident nun in charge of each, who was in loco parentis providing pastoral and religious support, if required. The convent, therefore, housed the rest of the small order of nuns, including those who had effectively 'retired', or stepped down from mainstream duties due to age-related health conditions. Also included were, of course, the resident staff, all of whom, like me, occupied some of the cubicles where once the nuns themselves had slept.

With breakfast over I was beginning to feel very fortunate in having eaten so well during the last twenty-four hours. I had not been used to seeing such a lavish variety of foods to choose from. At home, we ate good, basic home-cooking, but we ate what we were given, and no choices were ever afforded, nor were we ever asked what we would like to eat. Most of these students looked as if they were used to seeing a variety of foods from which to choose. It was as if it was all so normal.

Returning to my cubicle at almost ten o'clock I realised that I had hardly given a thought to Sean until now. I wondered where he had slept, and how he was managing to eat, given that his money would be running short, and especially whether he had found a young men's hostel for night stays. How fortunate I felt now, having had a good sleep, eaten some nourishing food, and enjoyed an utterly self-indulgent, deep, warm bath. I knew that I was a long way from being able to climb the upper echelons of Maslow's Hierarchy of Needs, but my situation was improving, thanks to the Sisters of Mary Immaculate.

The night before, having enjoyed my bath, I had hand-washed the clothes which I had been wearing since I had set off from Manchester. I had nowhere to hang them properly, and I didn't particularly want to enquire about laundry facilities. Neither did I relish the prospect of leaving what few items of clothing I had about, in what appeared to be this vast building, for all to see. Hence, I brought my washed, rinsed and hand-wrung items of clothing back up to my cubicle, and weighted down each piece of damp clothing so that it could hang and, hopefully, dry within a few days. Jesus had come in particularly handy in holding down my knickers and two nylon stockings. My other clothes were draped around this tiny space, from the table, the chair, and the bed rails. I seriously hoped that no one would catch sight of them, and especially the nuns who almost certainly would not wish the spectacle of Jesus Christ to be sullied with the accoutrements of my underwear.

That evening, after we had all completed our work for the day I joined the other resident staff in their communal sitting room. It was a simple facility, rather like the dormitory itself: the walls were plain and unadorned. Heavy, worn velvet curtains hung from the window which overlooked part of the back of the Convent. There was a table, on which an untidy pile of board games, playing cards and jigsaws were stacked, and several plain armchairs were placed around the room. In the corner sat a tiny old black and white television, which the scowler informed me didn't work properly because of flashing horizontal lines ruining the picture. I suggested that the Sisters might perhaps consider having it repaired for them, to which she scoffed and muttered:

'No chance,' and quickly turned her attention back to the Tarzan annual she was holding.

Meanwhile Aggie and Connie were engaged in their own, private world of giggling, and puerile utterances. Minnie flicked through a copy of Woman's Own magazine and Dorothy sat silently crocheting, unaware that her ball of purple wool had rolled over to the other side of the room. There was a large old wireless which rested on top of an inbuilt cupboard next to the fireplace but I imagined that most of the staff might find it difficult to concentrate, and listen to, a radio programme of any description.

Aggie and Connie continued to dominate the sounds and goings on of the sitting room, with their continuous, immature giggling. They began a game of 'tig', still seated, tapping each other, and then kicking each other as their hysterical laughter reached a pitch that I felt I could no longer tolerate. The others looked as if they hardly noticed the infantile behaviour of their colleagues, seemingly inured to it, each of them engaged in their own, interior world. I wished them good night and left the room. No one acknowledged my words, or even looked up to reciprocate.

This was a strange world, I reflected. Had the Sisters rescued these people from being placed in an even harsher establishment, such as an asylum? I found myself wondering whether they had been deposited, or taken in by the nuns, many years previously by families who had rejected them. In the case of the older lady, Dorothy, I wondered whether her marriage had failed, or if she had been widowed and become destitute with nowhere else to go. I couldn't imagine that the nuns paid them much, if anything at all. Whatever misfortunes had brought them here, the fact was, they were all fully institutionalised into the life at the convent, and the nuns' routine. Interestingly, also, it was *their* labour that fuelled the entire nuns' mission.

As the days in the convent passed, I began to think, more and more, about my parents and the fact that my sister Jean must have told them that I was no longer staying at her house. She will have informed them that I had left quietly, with no explanation of where I was going, or having given an address where I could be contacted. My conscience began to prick me. I kept pushing to the back of my mind the idea that I should at least write to my parents to tell them where I was now, and that I was safe and well, if only for my mother's sake. I knew that she would be worried about me, not knowing my whereabouts.

Importantly also, I felt a gnawing sense of duty that I should let my parents know what I hadn't dared to tell them when I had lived nearer to them: that I was expecting a baby. This would not be intended to summon help because I knew, without any shred of doubt, that there would be absolutely none offered. In fact, my father had always espoused the dictum that 'if you make your bed, then you have to lie on it'. In any case, I reasoned, I was far enough away from my father to know that he couldn't hurt me now. Distance had somehow given me the courage to confirm what may have been their worst fears.

The letter was polite, and respectful, as always, asking about their welfare and that of my younger sister Kay, adding also that I was in good health too, before informing them that I was in the capital; that I was working for an order of Roman Catholic nuns, with whom I was staying temporarily. I chose my words very carefully, writing and rewriting drafts in which I tried different ways of telling the enormity of my situation, so as to underplay its shocking truth. At the same time I wanted to let them know how much I wanted to have this baby. I concluded with a brief 'PS.', informing them that I had felt it necessary to tell a 'white lie'. That I had told the nuns that I was married, and I was known as Mrs Susan Delaney.

Licking the first class stamp and pressing it firmly on to the envelope, I felt a sense of 'Voila.' There it is. I've done it now. I felt relieved of my secret, purged of a truth that I no longer wanted to conceal. And if my father deigns to reply, I thought, however crushing its contents, I can find a way to live with it and somehow improve my lot as I move towards the birth of my child.

I didn't have to wait long before I found a letter which had been placed on my bed, stamped with a Manchester postmark. It was addressed to me, Mrs Susan Delaney, for which I felt grateful.

I stared at it for a moment. I sat down on the bed and looked at the familiar handwriting. It was Dad's, of course. The familiar, distinctive flourishes of his handwriting told me that it was his hand. A pang of anxiety gripped my stomach as I slid open the letter.

My father began by telling me that all three of them were well. He went on to say that they had suspected that I had gone away because of 'something like that', as he framed it. He also said that he had telephoned my former place of work, The Sun Alliance Insurance Company, where he had been informed that I had left their employ several weeks before. Knowing his way of thinking, there would have to be a serious reason or 'problem' for me to give up a very good, respectable job, and it could only be *that*.

Until well beyond the nineteen eighties, many thousands of pregnant girls and young women moved away from their homes, to another area where they would not be known, because of the social stigma attached to unmarried motherhood. These women were persecuted for what was seen as their immorality. The men who impregnated them were able to continue to live their unblemished, unaffected lives with no cessation to their jobs and careers, without the worry and distress associated with upheaval and loss at a particularly difficult time, since many young women were forced, or coerced into giving up their babies.

Referring to my wish to keep my baby, my father advised me to think very carefully about the matter; he stated that I could either have my baby and then give her or him up for adoption, or get married to Sean, and keep my baby. With both these 'options' there was an implication that, whichever of the two I chose to do, I should do it independently of them. Furthermore, the question of keeping my baby and staying single was never an option. I remember feeling very strongly that I could never give up my baby, and yet I didn't want to marry Sean. I had no idea how I was going to resolve the issue because in those days the very idea of co-habiting couples was also socially unacceptable outside marriage. Furthermore, it was always the *woman* in such a scenario who would be seen as nothing short of a 'harlot'.

I remembered when, only a few years' previously, a certain well-known male singer, a falsetto yodeller, no less, came to move in with a single woman two streets away from my childhood home. The gossip was almost deafening, and kept the whole neighbourhood chewing over the fat for a long time, regarding how 'brazen' she had to be in 'living over the brush', as it was called by many, *and* to a married man!

I sat for a long time reading, and re-reading between the lines, every word that Dad had written. At least he had not 'read the Riot Act' to me, and he wasn't threatening, or being unkind to me, but instead discharging what he felt was apt, fatherly advice. It left me with an ongoing conundrum. How could I possibly keep my baby, find suitable accommodation and appropriate childcare whilst undertaking a job in which I could earn enough money to look after us both? I hadn't reached that point yet, and when I did, I would hope for some sort of divine intervention.

On my second Sunday in the convent I woke, as usual, at six o' clock, and got ready for my first shift of the day, serving breakfast to a relaxed crowd of international female students. They were particularly noisy today, no doubt enjoying the prospect of their second day of the weekend, and planning new outings into the capital's hot spots. It was a warm day, and many of them looked lovely, dressed in beautiful clothes. They lined up at the end of the counter, and practised their newly acquired English language skills between themselves, and with me too as they pointed out which foods they would like to eat. I had learned how to key into their respective accents, as they searched for the right words and expressions to use.

French had been my favourite subject at school, and it had become one of my choices to study at Advanced Level. Sadly, my studies had come to an abrupt end when I felt compelled to leave school early to find work so that I could leave home and live independently. I had loved the idea that I would one day travel, and be able to use my French language skills to achieve greater fluency. I admired these young women and I was aware that this experience would equip them in their later careers, if they managed to break through the social barriers that might restrict their life choices. I had almost finished my stint at the counter when Mother Superior came sweeping into the service area to speak to me.

'Good morning, Susan. Great news for you!' she announced. 'Your husband is outside, asking to see you. I believe he has found you both a place to live!'

For a moment, it felt as if my heart must have stopped beating. It was just long enough for me to feign a smile. 'Oh!' I said, 'Well, I'll just finish off here and be down, right away, Mother.'

'Not at all', she said, 'I'll get one of the others to take over here. You must go to see him straight away.'

I tugged at the press studs at the sides of my tunic, and made my way pensively to the front door. Out in the brilliant sunshine, gazing upwards at the front door, there was Sean, smiling, and eager to see me. I smiled back, but within me churned a frenzied uncertainty.

'I've found us a room, Sue, and I have a permanent job. Well, it's as permanent as it can be, anyway. And my God, let's look at you, you're blossoming and happy with our baby. Are ye pleased to see me?' He took hold of me and lifted me off my feet, baby and all.

'Yes, 'course I am,' I said. 'Where is it?'

'Notting Hill Gate. Now, it's nothing special, just a room and we share a bathroom, but it's a start.'

As I opened the door into my little cubicle for the last time I looked around and felt an overwhelming sense of sadness. I had to go. I had to see if Sean could hold down a steady job, something which he hadn't seemed to do very well in Manchester. I had to see also if he could curb his drinking. If he could be responsible, and start to restrain his hot-headed temperament, and not be so possessive. I had once loved him for his good spirits and sense of fun. But I had also seen an impetuosity, a bad temper when he had drank too much, and the headstrong, wilful side of him that unnerved me.

I bid my farewell and my thanks to Sister Keiran, Sister Cecelia and Mother Superior, in particular, and although I had met many of the other nuns it was these three with whom I had become familiar, and who had each played a tiny part in my life and my recovery, though they didn't know it. I simply waved to all the staff who saw me leave, who were probably used to seeing the odd soul come and go, and who probably did not understand, or care less that I was moving on to another sort of existence.

CHAPTER 4

Sean and I walked for over an hour to Notting hill Gate to the house where our new home awaited us. We stopped at Hyde Park so that I could have a brief rest. It never occurred to us to take the tube. To walk was what came naturally. I was surprised and really glad that Sean had carried my suitcase all of the way there. Perhaps this was a sign of better things to come: that he was he trying to demonstrate our new beginning. A fresh start.

Notting Hill Gate was not the trendy place it has now become. It was inhabited not by the well-heeled set but, I gleaned, by people who were passing through, working or staying in London en route to other places. Sean took me to a large, established terrace house in the middle of a row of other, similar properties. It was sub-divided into individually rented rooms and our room was on the first floor. We had access to shared bathroom facilities.

Each room was, essentially, a bed-sit. Ours was furnished with a cooker and a sink and draining board on one side of the room, and a double bed, a slim wardrobe and a tiny table on the other. The floor was fitted with linoleum, and there was a big bay window looking out on to a landscape of houses. The room was not smart-looking, but it was adequate. There was no television, and we both agreed that perhaps we would gauge whether we could afford to rent one in a few weeks' time.

'Sue, a really nice Portuguese couple live just below us. I had a brief chat with them the other day and they're looking forward to meeting you.'

This sounded promising, I thought. Maybe we could even become friends.

He had been working on the building site, as a hod-carrier and general labourer. I knew that he was happy working outdoors, and he felt comfortable doing that work. He was quick, fit and strong, and this work paid good money.

My role was understood. We both knew that it would have been impossible for me to find work as a pregnant, single woman, with National Insurance Cards which confirmed my unmarried status, and especially also for only just a few months. Sean was earning enough for the two of us to get by, and he was happy for me to take care of all the domestic chores.

I soon found the nearest shops where I could get basic provisions. Sean gave me some housekeeping money every Friday and I had to make the money last until his following week's pay day came around.

Only a short walk away were the Butcher's, Grocer's and a Greengrocer's shops. Because fridges and freezers came much later for most of the working classes, I went shopping daily to buy the fresh food required for each day, as did my mother before me. It was also an opportunity to get out from within the four walls of our room. I took our washing to a local launderette each week, and washed and dried our clothes and bed linen in next to no time. Every day I dusted, swept and mopped out the room, and the first floor landing also and, in addition, I cleaned the communal stairs and the bathroom, every few days. I prepared and cooked a hot meal ready for when Sean came home, and made a packed lunch for him to take to work the next day. I did what every good housewife did, and I took pride in doing it all well, so that Sean's life was comfortable and fully 'serviced'.

Sean had some Saturdays and every Sunday off work, and at the weekend he was keen for us go out to one of the nearby pubs in the evening, to spend an hour or two enjoying the relaxed atmosphere, and perhaps listening to some music. Sometimes a folk or a jazz band came to play, and he liked the Irish pubs where bands would sing the songs that reminded him of home. I too had become fond of Irish music. The songs would invariably be about life, love, loss and death; all things human, that touched me and my interests, my sensibilities.

My maternal grandfather had been a tour guide in his later years for Thomas Cooke and my mother used to tell me how much he had particularly enjoyed accompanying the coach tours to Ireland. He was especially drawn to the country's literary heritage, and of course, jolly evenings in which there was plenty of 'the craic', as the Irish call it. For the Irish, however, this term means far more than about that of having a good time, but is inextricably linked to their roots of story telling, history and music.

During the first year after meeting Sean we went to see the famous Irish band, The Dubliners, perform in Manchester. Sean said that their hit song: *'The Black Velvet Band'* would always remind him of me because I wore such a ribbon in my long brown hair.

He had painted an intriguing story of his homeland, telling me much about his life and his large family, and the significance of the Catholic church which played a major role in the lives of everyone, from birth to the grave. His descriptions about people generally, and a community in which everyone was known, and of neighbours who would look out for, and support everyone else, held a particular fascination for me. I hoped that one day I could visit this nearby country which was so much a part of Sean and which had won the affections of my grandfather also.

On our first Friday evening together after I had moved in, we made our way to a local pub. There was a lively, noisy atmosphere. Most people had finished work for the week and wanted to relax, talk, and sing along to the music of the resident folk artists. I was not drinking alcohol but, as usual, Sean was drinking pints of Guinness, which he did with alarming gusto. Although I enjoyed the music I was feeling tired, and sitting on a stool for long periods wasn't much fun for me. I understood that he had worked hard all week, and sitting in our room in the evenings and retiring early to bed when he had an early start the next day was bearable, but at weekends he was keen to enjoy an evening out. I tried to perk up for Sean's sake.

When Sean had downed a few pints he sometimes became restless and challenging, and tonight was no exception. As we walked home he turned and spoke abruptly:

'Why are you so fucking miserable?' he said. I had learned from old that I had to temper my answers so as not to exacerbate any potentially volatile situation.

'I'm not, Sean. I'm just tired, that's all. I did enjoy the music, though, didn't you?

He carried on, picking fault, and I thought that if anyone looked miserable it was him, but I brushed it aside, trying to lift things.

'Shall we get some chips?'

He said he didn't want to walk as far as the nearest chip shop, and so we turned into our road, and I suggested that maybe I could make us both a sandwich. I realised that I was humouring him. This wasn't a good sign for our future, but I hoped that it was simply a blimp.

When we opened the door to our room, Sean said that he just wanted to go to bed. I made some tea, but by the time I placed his cup down he was sound asleep.

Being there in that tiny room together was difficult for both of us. Sean had days of hard, physical work, and though he was pleased to be in work and earning a good wage, I could understand that a quiet room in Notting Hill Gate was hardly the hive of activity that he had been used to in his home in Ireland. It wasn't as if I had any interesting news to tell him about my day. I tried, of course, but a shopping trip where my only discourse with other people involved two pork chops and a pound of veg. hardly provided me with fodder for interesting repartee.

Sean, on the other hand, had lots to tell me. He would often tell me jokes that the other builders had shared between themselves during the day, most of which were very rude, but nevertheless funny. Because he was the youngest worker on the site the other men would poke fun at him in friendly banter, and even that invariably involved sexual innuendo intended to tease or embarrass him. He would bring it all home, and we would laugh together at the outrageousness of it all, as I imagined the scenes: Sean, carrying huge weights of bricks and mortar up steep ladders to the top of a high wall while some smart Alec held a running commentary on his supposed libido and how tired he looked that day.

Each day was very much like the next for me. Though at the time I didn't realise it, I was quite lonely. I drifted from one dull task to another, trying to do my best, but hoping that life would change for the better. I too was in an alien place, far from my own home town and the familiar, people and places I knew. I went through the same motions every day, not seeing a soul but the shopkeepers. I looked forward to the evenings when Sean would tell me about his work and about aspects of some of his co-workers and their lives, together with more of their ribald humour that I had come to expect.

I could have happily skipped going to the pub at weekend, but it was what Sean wanted to do, and so I would get changed and try to look nice, despite my swelling abdomen.

One Saturday evening I knew that Sean was tired but he insisted that we go out. He needed a pint, he said, which naturally meant more than one, in fact considerably more, in this instance. He was drinking his fourth pint of the evening, at a rate which I could tell was going to include more. He suddenly leaned towards me and said:

'Yeah, he's a good-looking fella, isn't he?' looking over towards a group of people nearby.

''Who?' I said, knowing exactly to whom he was referring, because although we were surrounded by men, one particular young man was seated at the next table, close to my line of vision as I watched the lively band ahead. I was never, for a moment, in the habit of staring at other men. Furthermore, knowing Sean so well, with his insecurities and his jealous streak, I always made a point of concentrating my gaze well away from other males, as best I could, and especially ones that might be considered attractive.

Sometimes, it wouldn't matter if the male in question was far from good-looking. He would accuse me of trying to beguile and seduce them, trying to humiliate *him*, and wanting to be given a 'good time,' as he put it, when the truth that I had no wish whatsoever to encourage *anyone* to look at me, let alone anything more. Long before I became pregnant he expressed groundless fears about how he could see that different men clearly found me attractive because they had looked at me more than once. This always occurred when he was under the influence of alcohol. The whole issue was ludicrous. It was always made worse if another man gave me a second look, and this could be completely innocent. He would turn the thing around by accusing *me* of encouraging them; or reciprocating, or finding them more attractive than *he* was. The fact that I was heavily pregnant made no difference to his accusations.

Sean's possessiveness had become more extreme since he had been working on the building site. It seemed that the men with whom he worked had nothing but sex on their minds all day long, such was the endless sexually-charged banter, and the calls and wolf whistles to women in the street who had the temerity to walk past the site. Any unsuspecting victim would be regaled with comments about her bosom, her rear, her legs or clothes, and whatever else they could think of that they thought might elicit a response, such as: 'Give us a smile, darlin', it may never happen,' when it just *had*. It amounted to what I regarded was a verbal assault on women, usually with sexual connotations, which I always believed was part of a 'herd' mentality, and what amounted to men's need to validate their misguided notions of their own masculinity. All those, half-stripped, bronzed, would-be Adonis', or maybe Burt Reynolds', seriously believing that they were God's gift to all women, had big problems, I thought.

I became convinced that this working environment only served to exacerbate Sean's insecurities.

On that particular Saturday night, as Sean became more inebriated, his rhetoric not only continued unabated, but he became increasingly abusive towards me. I began to feel very anxious and distressed. Trying simply to allay his fears did not reassure him. He knew that he was being unkind, and that I was upset. I didn't feel able to say that I wanted to go back to our room, because I was worried that it might continue there, and I wanted desperately for it to stop before we were indoors.

We walked back towards the terraced property. He was decidedly drunk and unsteady on his feet. He continued to accuse me of wanting to be unfaithful. My usual ploys to try to distract him, or make him laugh weren't working. We came to a bench at the top of a hill, not far from where we lived, and I promptly sat down on it.

'What the fuck are you doing?' he shouted, landing clumsily beside me.

'I'm taking a breather, looking at this landscape,' I answered. Of course, I was doing no such thing. I was stalling for time.

'Well it's fucking nothing to write home about, you know that,' he said and, then, trying to soften his approach, he whimpered 'Come on, Sue. I'm tired. You must be tired. Let's go back to the room, and go to bed.'

I wasn't convinced by his pretence at making peace. He had said so many terrible things at the pub, *and* all the way home; accusing me of many dreadful deeds. He had also called me so many disgusting names, that I felt that he had gone too far this time, and it would only lead to his casting more dreadful aspersions, and I feared that his temper might boil over in the room.

We sat for a while in silence. Looking askance I could see that his eyes closed, and his chin fell to rest on his chest. His breathing became slower, and I realised that he had fallen asleep. Minutes later a group of revellers passed by and he was jolted from his drunken slumber, and realised that we were still sitting on the bench.

The chilly night air was bracing enough to clear his head just a little, so I began, gently:

'You know, Sean,' pausing for a moment. 'I don't deserve that treatment. All that pent up anger and the sheer injustice of all those terrible things you said. You know that I'm not like that, at all. So why do you say those hurtful things?'

'I know,' he said. 'Now let's go home and go to bed.' There was no remorse. Sean could not bring himself to apologise. He was now simply cold, uncomfortable and tired. He was beginning to sober up and he was in need of sleep.

I needed to go to the toilet, but I was still worried that there might be a flicker of anger that he might want to take out on me, and so I held out, under the guise of wanting to discuss our relationship. I would have liked to have received unprompted assurances that he regretted his cruel words, and that there would be no more of them. But he was beyond reasoning, beyond thinking clearly and fairly, and after a protracted period of time, when all the world seemed to be sleeping, I rose, and he quietly followed me back to the room that we shared. I was nervous, and unsure of what to expect, however after going to the bathroom he took off his clothes and climbed into bed.

I lay in bed, staring up at the ceiling, exhausted by the awful events of the evening, and worried about where this would eventually lead to. Was he feeling 'trapped' by my pregnancy? Did he fear that his youth and his freedom, and opportunity for fun had gone, and perhaps he felt he was just not ready for fatherhood?

If only I had been able to ask him that, because, in fact, I didn't think that he *was* ready for the responsibility. I wanted to say to him that it was okay, because if we could both figure a way of existing separately with some support for me initially, then that would be fine with me. In an ideal world a woman would want to be closely involved with the father of her child, but if that meant being regularly subjected to abuse, or cruel treatment, then the former arrangement would be preferable.

But I couldn't ever say that. He would be totally affronted. There would most likely follow:

'So you don't think I'll make a good father? You don't want me in your life. Is that it? I was right all along, wasn't I? You actually want to have other men, don't you?'

I agonised over whether I should raise the whole matter again when we woke up.

The sun was streaming through the curtains. Sean woke me up with a cup of tea, and put his hand on mine. 'Sue, I'm truly very sorry for last night. I didn't mean any of it.'

'So why do you say such dreadful things?'

'Me darlin' girl. I must be mad,' he said. 'It's just that I can't bear to see other men leering at you.'

'But, he wasn't, Sean. He was just looking around, enjoying the atmosphere. Why would he blatantly do that in front of you?'

'You don't know how a young fella thinks,' he insisted.

'Well, is that how *you* think?'

'Look, the sun is shining,' he said. 'It's a gorgeous day. We should take a walk somewhere. There are lots of parks around here. Maybe we could find somewhere nice to sit and have an ice cream, or something. Maybe have a bite to eat somewhere? Come on, Sue, let's enjoy this day off together.'

I sipped my tea while he made his way to the bathroom. I wanted things to work. I wanted to have a lovely relationship with him, and for us both to look forward to having this wonderful event that was about to happen. But, now, again, there were the seeds of doubt about whether or not he could control his drinking habits and deal with his irrational thoughts and behaviour. It wasn't as if *I* had a choice in what I did. If anyone was trapped in a situation it was *me*. Okay, I had resolved that I wanted my baby, but without the means and the opportunity to live independently where did that leave me?

I got up and half-heartedly picked out some clothes from my limited selection hanging in the wardrobe. Mum would have said: 'Chin up, Susan. Worse things happen at sea. Try to put it all behind you.'

As things transpired, we both had a lovely day. We walked to Hyde Park, and sat in the sunshine, watching families with their children, and toddlers learning to walk. Sean clearly loved children, and coming from a very large family he could hardly escape them, but he really did have a knack of relating to young children, playing games with them and making them laugh, especially. Around mid-day he suggested that we go into a little cafe and have a light bite to eat, which was a treat for both of us.

Sean and I were grounded in the everyday; in a tiny microcosm of repeated behaviours. We were, of course, very young, still finding out about each other, still learning about that tiny niche of a much larger, gigantic capital city. We were playing safe, rather than experimenting with our access to the wider community and different experiences elsewhere.

Get-togethers of all descriptions had occurred in Sean's life, and he missed the coming together of familiar groups in which he was known and loved. My family, with all of its weaknesses and flaws, did not engage in pub-going. Very occasionally, such as at Christmas time, or during a holiday away my father might spend an hour in a pub, but it was rare. Sean's family, however, and his community, was steeped in the rituals of frequenting public houses, especially if there was something to celebrate, and there was *always* something to celebrate. Children were allowed in bars, and so the culture was self-perpetuating.

He had told me about his growing up and his family in great detail, with such obvious affection. He found, in work, some sort of camaraderie, albeit not the most wholesome. Without expressing it I felt he yearned for his life back home.

He had originally come to England to find work, to earn money and also to seek whatever excitement and fun he could derive from the bigger cities over here. As time wore on, however, I sensed that he missed home far more than he had envisaged.

My situation was quite different. Naturally, I felt displaced and unfamiliar with this life I was carving, but because I had been brought up in a small family setting, with no nearby relatives. I was used to a quieter existence, and I was prepared to endure the duller aspects of life, knowing that we could work at shaping our world for the better, and for that of our child to come.

Another weekend loomed. Once again, he was keen to try out another pub about which one of his co-workers had told him. It was a Saturday evening, four weeks into our Notting Hill Gate life together, and Sean was in good spirits, looking forward to a night out together and some music. I played along with the idea, though I could happily have rested with my feet up, reading a newspaper or just chatting. I was almost seven months' pregnant by this time.

The place turned out to be a good recommendation for the music scene. There was a small group of accomplished, amateur musicians with a female lead singer who sang some of the politically inspired songs of Joan Baez, and those of Joni Mitchell too, with a mix of The Mamas and Papas' songs thrown in for good measure.

I loved the music, and Sean seemed to enjoy the atmosphere too. I felt that he seemed to be taking longer to drink each pint, and he stayed in good spirits. We stayed until the landlord rang time on a huge bell behind the bar, and then we gathered our things and left to begin our walk home.

Thankfully, this time, Sean seemed to have drank less than on previous occasions. It was still enough to render the most ardent beer-drinker legless, and I was beginning to realise the full extent of his need and capacity to drink heavily. We had the usual conversation about whether to stop for fish and chips, or wait until we got back to the room to have a sandwich or some cheese on toast and a cup of tea. We settled for the latter, and finished the walk back to the house.

I was glad to get back. I was very tired, and relieved that the evening had worked out well. I was certainly under that impression but, as I was to discover, I couldn't have been more wrong.

No sooner had we closed the door to our room, but Sean started to become provocative again.

'So, tell me now, who were you looking at every time I went to the bar?'

My heart sank somewhere down to my knees. Oh no, not all that again, I thought.

'Sean, how can you start this, again? You think that I waited for you to disappear to the bar before trying to eye up someone, or was it more than *one* man this time?' I said, sarcastically. 'I didn't look at anyone! I had a lovely time, listening to the music. I think that you're over-tired.'

'The big blonde-looking fella who was sitting at the table opposite! The one with the big shoulders and puffed out chest.'

'Oh, come on, Sean, stop making all this up.' I felt weary with this whole saga, but I was also already starting to feel anxious.

'You know exactly who I'm talking about,' he shouted, 'because I saw him looking back at you. You must think I'm fucking green.'

I sat down on the edge of the bed in sheer exasperation, holding my head in my hands. Yes, there was certainly a man of Sean's description sitting at the table opposite ours. But there were men everywhere, as there were women, and I had certainly not stared, or tried to catch the eye of *any* man. I wasn't interested in *anyone*, and I couldn't believe he was imagining, *again,* that anything of the sort he was suggesting had happened.

Had he been thinking this, all the way home, chewing over this fantastical non-event over and over, holding back especially until we got indoors before he could spew it all out angrily and take out his pent up anger on me? Why would he do that?

I tried the last resort. If humouring doesn't work try injecting the absurd, the farcical, was frequently my way of trying to take the edge out of a situation: 'Look, Sean, we're both tired. This is stupid. I'm almost seven months' pregnant and let's face it I look like an oversized shallot! What perv would take a second look at me anyway? Don't spoil things again. I'll make a cup of tea and we'll ……….' Just as I had begun to lift myself from the bed I felt a crashing thud to my face, a strike so fierce that it threw me flat on my back, on to the bed.

'You lying bitch,' he shouted. 'Girls like you should be on the streets, where you belong!'

In sheer disbelief I stared upwards at the old light pendant which was swaying from side-to-side, suddenly realising that he had hit me. In a split second another savage blow smashed into my face, seeming to come from nowhere.

'Please, *stop*, Sean,' I cried, now hurt and scared. 'I'm with *you!* You're the father of our baby,' I wailed, incredulously. 'Why are you doing this?' In a flash, he jumped on to the bed next to me, and knelt astride me, still shouting and swearing and, before I could comprehend the horror of what he was about to do next, his fist came down hard, deliberately into my swollen abdomen.

'*Please, the baby!*' I screamed, recoiling to one side, 'I'm going to lose it, please! Don't kill the baby! *Don't!*' I lay, sobbing, captive, wondering what I was supposed to do.

Everything happened so swiftly. I couldn't think straight.

Sean jumped off the bed and rushed over to the corner of the room where my case was standing. He was yelling and shouting obscenities. He pulled it open and, snatched at its contents, proceeding to break and tear apart everything that was left in it: he ripped to small shreds some family photographs, he stamped on a spiral gold ring that had once belonged to my late grandfather, completely destroying it; he ripped apart some accessories, some letters and childhood keepsakes, and grasped anything else that he thought to be of value to me that he could ruin. He then grabbed hold of the wardrobe door and pulled out what remained of my clothes and, one-by-one ripped them apart, all the while swearing and calling me the most sickening names. Terrified, I lay still, not daring to move or to say anything more in case he hit me again. In a state of abject shock, and distress, I watched him as he rampaged through my things.

In the midst of this savagery all that I could think about was my baby. Nothing else mattered. Will I abort the baby?' Inwardly I panicked. He didn't stop until most of what I owned was completely ruined.

I lay despairingly on the bed, silently sobbing, and petrified, I didn't dare to move an inch.

After this deranged fit, when there seemed nothing else of mine to destroy, quite suddenly, he seemed to run out of steam. Slumping down on to the bed, spent, he rolled away from me, and fell into an exhausted, drunken sleep.

I lay motionless, terrified that he would open his eyes and turn to me again to give vent to more anger. My top lip, and the skin above my lip was wet. When I wiped my hand slowly across my face, trying not to disturb this man now seemingly comatosed next to me, the blood dripped from my face and my hand, on to the bed. I didn't care. All I cared about was that my baby should survive the impact in his amniotic fluid. I pictured my baby, hoping that s/he had lain at such an angle in the sac that not only would that still be intact, but also that it had protected his or her head and that the blow did not amount to a serious wound. I knew that I needed a miracle. I also knew that it might take a while before signs of miscarriage would become apparent. I prayed a sobbing, pleading silent prayer asking God to spare my baby.

I had to try to escape; to break free of all of this. But if I rushed for the door he might wake up and block my exit, and I would risk more violence. I had to bide my time. I had to stem my sobs and my shaking, and breathe as smoothly as I could. We were both lying on the bed in the clothes in which we had gone out. At least, I thought, I have the clothes I'm wearing so that I can get out into the street. My shoulder bag lay down the side of the bed closest to me where I had let it slip when Sean started to shout. I had just one pair of footwear, sandals that he hadn't destroyed, still dangling from my toes. As soon as I was absolutely sure that he was in the soundest of sleeps I would try to make for the door, and hope he wouldn't wake up at that point, and drag me back.

I lay for what seemed to be an eternity, taking the greatest of care not to move or tilt the mattress, or risk in any way stirring him from sleep. My left hand slowly slipped down to the floor from the edge of the bed beside me, and without looking, or turning, I carefully, gently, looped the strap on to my hand. Everything had to move at a snail's pace. Painstakingly, I eased my body up from the bed, then slowly rose to my feet. Silently creeping along as in some animated slow-motion film, I finally reached for the door handle, leaving the devastation of broken and shredded wreckage behind. Once outside, I closed the door with the same, patient deftness that I had practised as a child when Dad used to make me open and close the door a hundred times in punishment for allowing the door to be banged shut by the wind.

This protracted departure took every ounce of energy I had left in me. I tip-toed slowly along the landing, escaping downstairs to another bathroom I knew to be on the floor below. Once inside, I slid the lock closed, sat down on the toilet and, with my shaking legs apart to keep my balance, wept uncontrollably.

I must have stayed in there for another hour, bathing my face, trying to breathe calmly and trying to straighten myself up. My eyelids were swollen, and there were enormous bags of puffy, water-filled skin under my eyes. I looked as if I had gone several rounds with boxing champion Sugar Ray Robinson. A long, bloody cut that ran from my top lip up to my nose at an angle was swollen and sore, and under my pan stick makeup there was some bruising, that only I knew was there.

Sitting on the toilet, with my head leaning to one side on to the bathroom wall I tried to think rationally. No waters had broken yet. There was no bleeding. 'Please, please God, make my baby alright,' I prayed over, and over again.

There was no telephone in the house and therefore I couldn't summon help quickly.

This, I resolved fiercely, was the end of our relationship. If my unborn baby survives this horrendous ordeal, I couldn't risk it ever happening again. Besides, now, I hated him. I wanted to go.

There was nothing else for it. I had to go back to Manchester and, with loss of face, I had to go and ask my parents to help me.

I had only the following week's housekeeping money, but I knew that it was enough to buy a one-way ticket on a National Express Coach to Manchester, Piccadilly, and then pay for a short bus ride to Audenshaw.

Eating away at me was the need to go back into the room to see if I could salvage anything of my belongings to take away with me. What lay upstairs was all I owned, and if I could find anything left at all of value to me, still intact, I felt compelled to at least try. I remembered that I had hung my lightweight coat behind the door, and couldn't remember him lunging to destroy it. There was also some bedding, washed and ironed, in the bottom of the wardrobe that Sean must have felt wasn't sufficiently personal or interesting enough to demolish. There were also some practical, kitchen items which I had brought with me from Manchester, and I knew that I was going to need those at some point.

Hurting, and still feeling shaky and traumatised, I knocked quietly on the door of the bed-sit of the young Portuguese couple. It was about four o' clock in the morning. Although I hadn't yet been able to meet them properly I thought that if, perhaps, I were to tell them everything, they might be able to accompany me so that I would be safe enough to go back into the room to check my belongings.

After several gentle knocks on their door, the young Portuguese man appeared, dressed in his pyjamas and, with the door open only slightly, he could see my ravaged face.

'Can you please help me?' I pleaded, as I tried not to start crying again. 'I'm in a bit of a mess.' He looked at me in puzzlement, then opened the door wider.

'What happened?' he questioned, looking concerned. 'Come in.' His wife sat up in bed, roused from sleep, and she asked too:

'What's wrong? Are you hurt?'

I couldn't hold back my tears. I had vowed not to cry any more, but I just couldn't help it. The stress of it all seemed to pour out of me.

His young wife climbed out of bed immediately and threw a dressing gown around her shoulders. 'I make some tea,' she said in her best English. 'You wait for tea. Please.' She put her hand on my shoulder, which only elicited more tears, together with snivelling, spluttered coughs.

I had some toilet paper which I had put into my bag from the bathroom and now used it all up to wipe my eyes again and blow my nose. I was conscious that the pan stick make-up had come off in my tissue and that I had probably exposed the full, technicolour of mess that I had tried so carefully to conceal.

A mug of hot tea was placed in my hand, and the young woman sat down on the end of the bed after placing their mugs nearby. I sipped. It was comforting. Just having someone want to listen, and seem to care, was heartwarming in itself. I sensed that they were both very nice, kind people who were genuinely alarmed by my distress and my appearance.

I apologised for having woken them up, before telling them an abridged version of the whole sorry story. I explained that I needed to just check my belongings to see if there were any things remaining that I could salvage before I left. After a few minutes I plucked up the courage to ask if one of them would be very kind and simply accompany me back to our room so that I could check. I assured them that Sean would not wish to hurt *them*, and was probably sobering up by this time.

Without a second thought the young man pulled on some trousers and a sweater over his pyjamas and slid his feet into some casual shoes. 'Okay, we go,' he said. His young wife extended her arms towards me, and pulled me close to her for a moment.

'Good luck. Please, care for yourself and your baby,' she said and, once again, I could feel the tears welling up again inside me.

As we left their room and started for the stairs, I looked up to find that Sean was standing on the landing above, clearly having woken up to find that I had left the room. Maybe he had heard stirrings below in the couple's room. As I reached the top, I brushed past him, looking straight ahead. In hushed tones I uttered that I had come to see if there was anything left for me to take.

He was silent. Arms folded, he hung his head, and said nothing. This time there could be no sobered apologies; nor excuses, regrets, or cajoling. No vow that he'll never do it again. He knew that I was determined to leave, and there would be no stopping me now.

CHAPTER 5

I knew my way to Victoria Coach Station. Sean and I had travelled twice before using National Express Coaches into London and back to Manchester. I remembered the bay where the coaches from Manchester pulled in. When I arrived there was a coach already stationed in there. I hastened to buy my ticket, just in time to see the driver climbing aboard, ready to depart.

I had a double seat to myself for most of the journey. Leaning back, knowing that I could have five and a half hours of uninterrupted time to rest should have been welcomed. But I felt at 'rock bottom'. Things couldn't get much worse than this, I thought. Had he secretly resented me, loathed me all along, to have perpetrated such heinous damage? I knew that he had grown up in poverty, and had been subjected regularly to physical violence as a child; but to inflict such harm upon someone for whom he had expressed so much love was unfathomable to me. And what was going to happen to me and my baby, I fretted.

I hoped that in this, my worst hour, Dad would allow me to stay under their roof, if only for a little while. The only problem was that he had recently sold our house, the home in which I was born, and grew up, but from the scant information that

Dad had written in his last letter to me, their plans had gone awry. His frail mother had previously agreed to live with them if they were to buy a larger house to accommodate her but, at the eleventh hour, she changed her mind. He had already signed the contract to sell. He had sold the house privately, probably due to his mistrust of Estate Agents, and not wanting to pay their fees. His handling of the whole transaction had lacked necessary business acumen and, as a result, they had to move out of our house before they were ready.

With my little sister Kay, they moved into temporary lodgings and all their furniture had to be put into storage facilities. It all sounded very strange to me, but I had been distracted by my own problems and I hadn't had the chance to speak to my mother, who may have been able to explain more. However, I knew that even if Mum *had* been able to speak more freely about it, she may not have felt able to go into detail. She was always conscious of 'towing Dad's line'. Dad always believed that one's personal business should be kept close to one's chest, and Mum would not wish to openly criticise him, or tell of any oversight he may have made in the whole business. Her loyalty, even in the face of his errors or weaknesses, was laudable. Or was it perhaps a fear of retribution, of one of his angry, protracted outbursts, were he to discover that she had 'spilled the beans' that accounted for her discretion in these matters?

Whatever their situation was now, and however my predicament pained and embarrassed them, theirs was the only port in my storm left in which to drop anchor.

When the coach reached Cheshire I began to feel more anxious. I reapplied my makeup in the hope that I could mask all the signs of injury to my face. I managed fairly well to cover the bruising, but even the thick, sixties' makeup couldn't completely conceal the bloody cut from my lip. I thought up a plausible story to try to account for the wound, and hoped that I wouldn't need to use it.

Earlier, on my way to Victoria Coach station I telephoned the house where my family were staying, asking to speak to my father. He sounded subdued and suspicious of my reasons for wishing to speak to him. I briefly told him that I was returning to Manchester and that I hoped to call and see them later in the afternoon. He had not asked any questions, and neither had I offered any explanation as to why I was planning a visit. It was polite and brief. I needed time to think of what I was going to say to them.

One thing that I felt sure of: I could not concede that the father of my baby had physically ill-treated me. I felt far too ashamed of it. After all, in Dad's way of thinking, not only had I *got myself* pregnant to a no-good foreigner, of whom he would never have approved, but to tell him the truth would only confirm how low his daughter had 'sunk.' Importantly, also, it would serve to reinforce his self-righteous, prejudiced beliefs that 'they' only come over to England to get work and drink heavily; that 'they' are foul-mouthed 'parasites' who bring their brawling, offensive behaviour to our country.

As I knocked on the door of their lodgings, I was very nervous and didn't know what to expect. As always, Dad took control. He opened the door, reservedly, and said very little. I was led into a small parlour, where Mum stood, ready and smiling, and she asked me how I was. Kay was nowhere to be seen. We were never a family of kissers, or huggers, so we all stood to attention for a moment, me holding my old brown suitcase, and my coat buttoned so as not to draw unwanted attention to my matronly shape.

'Yes, I'm fine, thank you,' I said, nodding and mustering a smile, trying to conceal the truth, that I felt like the absolute pits. Mum invited me to sit down at a table which looked set for a meeting. She then said that she would make us some tea, and promptly disappeared out of the room. Dad looked particularly awkward. He must have been gearing himself up to deal with this uncomfortable encounter. He asked where Sean was. For a girl who was brought up never to utter a lie I was getting very good at it. I answered that he was staying behind for a few weeks so that he could earn some extra money, and then he would be coming back up to Manchester, to join me.

A stultified, inane conversation regarding London ensued until Mum thankfully reappeared. She placed a tray on the table from which she lifted a teapot, three sets of cups and saucers and a milk jug. She positioned them carefully on to a crisp white-laced tablecloth, followed by a small plate of fig rolls and some tea plates.

'The thing is, Susan,' Dad started suddenly, 'as I've said to you before, you must either marry him,' managing this time to avoid saying his name, 'or you have the baby and have it adopted.'

Well that was that, I thought, 'simple.' Dad had all the answers. Everything was always expressed in colours of black and white. My humble feelings, my needs, my precious hopes and dreams didn't enter into the equation. As nervous as I was, I managed to utter, quietly, that I wanted to keep my baby. I didn't want to give her or him away. I didn't refer to Sean in my scheme of things. Why couldn't they read my face, or read between the lines and consider what I *wasn't* saying? Didn't they know me well enough to detect my anguish? That the thought of giving away this little life in me was unbearable? Dad shuffled in his seat uncomfortably and his voice became more urgent. He insisted:

'A woman can't live on her own and bring up a child! There's no way you could do it. How would you live? Where would the money come from to pay your rent, and all the bills and food?

You'd have to be in a place of your own and there's no way you could get one!'

He was, of course, referring not only to the seemingly impossible practicalities of caring for a child and paying my way, but especially also to the social prohibitions at that time. Unmarried mothers were generally shunned by society and no self-respecting landlord would let their property to such a morally undesirable tenant. Moreover, my father knew that, in the unlikely event that I did manage to find some accommodation, women's rates of pay were much lower than those of men's undertaking the same work, and would be insufficient to live on and support a child; something of which he would have approved, given that men were, as he would assert, *quite rightly*, the providers.

Worse thought still, he wouldn't want his own wife being 'saddled' with any child of mine to look after. That was a complete non-starter, and therefore he had reiterated my options, as he saw fit. Dad didn't enter into open discussions; he dealt with all of the women in his life as only an authoritarian would: *he* spoke his mind and, we, the distaff members of the family, were expected to take heed and abide by it.

Although at that time our welfare state was regarded as one of the best in the world, it still wasn't ready for family anomalies or aberrations. It would take a few more years before second-wave feminism inspired women to liberate themselves from terrible situations and put up with them no more. To cast away their ball and chains, and dare to break free from disastrous relationships.

'So what are your plans right now, until he comes back to Manchester?' Dad asked.

'I'm not sure,' I said. 'I don't have much money, and I....'

Dad suddenly rose to his feet, scraping back the chair and interrupting abruptly:

'You can't stay here. There are no spare rooms in this house. Anyway, I was looking up a place in the Yellow Pages earlier, where you could stay for a while 'til *he* comes up. Now, there'll be a bus running shortly into town and I'll go with you to find this place. We should just have enough time to catch the 216.'

Taking the queue I rose to my feet and, as I lifted my suitcase, Mum said:

'What's happened to your face, love?'

'Oh, this?' I queried, pointing to the gash from my top lip that resembled a flash of lightning. 'Well, I was just finishing off the mopping-out of the room yesterday, and when I bent down to catch the handle of the bucket I slipped on the wet floor and I went flying. As I did, I caught my face on the corner of the table. It didn't half hurt. In fact, it's still really sore today.' This well rehearsed line seemed to be believed. Mum commiserated. I detested myself for protecting the interests of a bully and a coward who had deliberately inflicted physical and emotional harm upon on me and, worse, compromised the life of his own baby-to-be.

But isn't that what women do, I reflected afterwards? Protect and lie to cover up the sins, fallibility and sheer blunders of the men in their lives, particularly when they are unworthy of us, and we know it?

I hadn't had enough of a clear head to think about what Dad had said in relation to where he wanted to take me. I just knew that I felt low, and sad that they didn't want me to stay under their roof. If there were no vacant rooms I would have slept on the floor. Or would that desperate measure only occur to someone who had been sleeping rough in London? Perhaps decent people wouldn't normally even consider the idea?

I hadn't seen any signs of the landlady they had spoken about. I hadn't even seen my own little sister. I supposed that was all part of the plan: Dad would most likely think that it wouldn't be a good idea for 'our Kay' to see her elder sister 'so indisposed', and especially to witness his intended solution to her problems. Neither would it look very good for them if they were to bump into the landlady, with their pregnant, unmarried daughter 'in tow', about to be shuffled off, out of the way.

I didn't know where Dad was taking me. I felt utterly wretched, and forlorn. A short bus ride later and we were in an insalubrious part of Manchester, with Dad carrying my case as we walked along a row of Victorian, municipal-type buildings in Long Millgate.

'This is it,' he acknowledged, staring up beyond some high steps to an austere-looking building. 'Here, take this,' he said, thrusting a number of coins into my hand. 'That'll pay for at least a few nights.'

I sloped after him up the steps, with a heart so heavy I could almost feel its weight in my chest. I wasn't going to let him see me cry. If I started, I knew I might never stop.

I didn't even know what the building was. Our footsteps echoed on the ancient tiled floor of a capacious entrance. A woman wearing a uniform came hurrying down a large stone staircase.

'Yes?' she enquired, her voice resounding around the open, high ceilinged, tiled hallway.

'My daughter is looking for a bed for the night,' said Dad.

The woman stepped inside a small office and quickly reappeared, requesting six shillings. I counted some of my coins on to a small counter and she handed me a ticket.

'Follow me' she said, without a smile or even a trace of humanity. As she mounted the steps, I followed, and Dad, carrying my case, was two steps behind me, until she turned around and admonished sharply: 'No. Not you,' she snarled, staring at my father. 'No men allowed up here. You'll have to go back down.'

There was an awkward silence, and Dad said: 'I'll go then, Susan.' He transferred my suitcase from his hand to mine. 'Let us know how things go,' he said, straight-faced. 'Drop us a line.' I nodded, unable to speak. I could have sworn that, behind his sombre countenance, I detected a momentary flicker of sadness. There was no goodbye. No kiss, of course. No hug. No outstretched hand. Having retreated, I can see his face clearly now, looking up at me from the austere entrance hall as I reached the top of the flight of commanding, cold steps, and looked down.

Turning again to follow the woman I didn't look back.

CHAPTER 6

The woman led me through a large, squeaking door, and up another flight of steps.

Finally we walked into a room divided by a gangway which separated two rows of dark, tarnished doors. She lifted the bunch of keys which hung from her waist, and unlocked one of them, pushing it back on its hinges to reveal the cubicle within.

'You'll be got up at seven in the morning,' she said, 'and vacate by eight-thirty, prompt. Right?'

'Yes. Thank you.' I didn't know how I would be 'got up', but at that moment I was too weary to care.

She appeared to have modelled herself along the lines of a prison warden. I closed the door, and listened to the sound of jangling keys fade into the distance. There was a tiny remnant of a sneck on the back of the door which I struggled to push upwards, hoping that it would be sufficient to lock it.

The cubicle looked very much like a prison cell I'd seen on television, minus a slop bucket. There was a narrow single bed, at the end of which was a tiny table and one upright chair, both facing a window against which thick iron bars had been fitted. Peering down through the bars I could see one of Manchester's narrow Victorian, murky alleyways. Directly across the alley, just a few yards opposite, stood another similarly depressing-looking ancient building, which blocked any direct sun light which might otherwise have crept through the bars.

I sat down on the edge of the bed, staring at the barred window. This place must be some sort of municipal hostel for destitute women, I presumed. It was unwelcoming, and it felt harsh. The last cubicle in which I had stayed, in London, had an entirely different feel to it. That one had represented a sanctuary, a safe place from which to start out anew. Not this time. Now, nearer still to the birth of my baby, I had been well and truly unceremoniously dumped; rejected, and every unspoken word had told me to 'get on with it'. The cubicle was similarly spartan as the last, but this one was minus Jesus. Minus all hope.

Alone again, tears trickled down my face and smarted the cut above my lip. They belonged not just to me but, I could have sworn, they were my baby's also.

This baby of mine was a survivor, I thought. A fighter. She or he had survived the most vicious of blows, and so had I. We belonged together.

'No one is going to take you away from me,' I vowed.

I sat, watching the last vestiges of light fade from the alleyway outside before climbing into the metal bed.

Rejection in one's darkest hour is the hardest pill to swallow. I knew that I would never forget this day. In my mind, it all seemed unreal, too shocking and awful to be real. But real it was.

A great, dark cloud of sadness enveloped me. Why didn't my parents care about me? I knew that Dad had taken control of this situation. That Mum didn't necessarily accord with his decision but, dominated as she was by him, she had to abide by him. Was it because, in Dad's eyes I had been 'sullied'?; that, now, I 'belonged' to another man? Didn't he care that I hurt? That I had once been a daughter who had made him laugh, and made him proud that I had done so well at school?

I concluded that Dad probably believed that, since I *was* now 'defiled' and in a predicament, I was someone's else's 'property'. My father absolved himself of all parental responsibility for me. Now '*he*' could take care of me.

As the night descended, with it came the banging and clanging of doors and rattling keys.

I lay in bed feeling that I had to find something to grasp, something to hold on to that would give me some tiny trace of hope. I wanted to pull something from the wreckage of the day.

Tears now dry I mused that, there can't be many people who can lay claim to have been so grievously afflicted in two different major cities on the same day, and live to tell the tale! I wanted to shout out that, surely, that fact merited an inclusion in the Guinness Book of Records!

My mind so stupefied, I flipped through almost every emotion imaginable.

Sadness now slowly turned to anger. It was a panacea for ill that has never failed me. Not one that I would suppose any psychologist would ever recommend; but just my own anti-dote to being kicked when I'm already down. What was that wonderful phrase that Oscar Wilde said, the quote which my fantastic English teacher told us?

'We are all in the gutter, but some of us are looking at the stars.'

'Well, me and you both, Oscar.' If I have to crawl out on my hands and knees, I thought, *I'll get out of this gutter.*

I got out of bed and fumbled in my pocket to check how much money I had left from the coins which Dad had put into my hand earlier. In the darkness I could see that there was enough left to buy another night in the hostel, with just a little over; and with the small amount also which I had left of the housekeeping money, after paying for fares, I worked out that I would probably have enough, overall, to buy another two nights' stay, *but* with nothing left to buy food. One more night's stay would mean that I could eat tomorrow *also*, if I was thrifty.

Back in bed, I resolved that there had to be a way of moving forwards. I was worthy of much more than this. After all, whatever *anyone else* thought of me, I knew that I was a good person. I knew that I was kind, and bright, and deeply sensitised to the world. I started to rack my brain for any chances of hope that I might have. I didn't think of myself as highly religious, but there seemed only the church to turn to.

Although I had been baptised an Anglican, Roman Catholic nuns had taken me into their convent in London, where I had been put to work, but even another experience like that would be infinitely preferable to living in *this* place, which appeared to me to teeter on the edge of the world. Maybe I could find another Roman Catholic facility that might help me here in Manchester? I thought that one thing was certain; it would help if I were to be able to catch hold of something, some rope to help me to pull myself out of 'my gutter'. Better than scuffing my knees, that's for sure.

I was still a minor; single, pregnant, and jobless; I had nowhere to live, or sleep, other than this terrible place. My options were limited, and I was fast running out of time and money.

There must be someone in this world who is compassionate and doesn't judge me adversely? Scouring the depths of my imagination, I finally mapped out a loose plan of action. I was desperate for sleep. I would refine my ideas in the morning. At least now I have the beginnings of a vague plan, I thought, as I finally drifted into a much-needed sleep.

No sooner, it seemed, had I fallen asleep but the night was pierced with terrifying screams! I woke, with startled alarm, to hear the most frightening, human, gurgling cries! It was three o' clock in the morning. My body seized rigid with shock, eyes staring into the darkness of the unfamiliar space, as the coarse cries seared through the night:

'Help me!....... Help me!.........Get off me! Get off me, you bastard! *Help!.........* *He's raping me!* Get off!......... Go away! *You bastard!*'

'Another raucous voice yelled '*Shut up!* Fucking *shut up!*'

'*He's raping me!* Sex! Sex! You just want me for sex! Get him *off* me! Get out of here! Get out! *Help me!......................*'

To my horror, more voices joined into a crescendo: '*Bitch! Bitch! Fuck off* and get out of here!'

Other women started groaning loudly, while more still began to scream shrill, animalistic noises. There seemed to be mass hysteria. There was no intervention, no warden apparently around to quell the mayhem. The yelling and high pitched screaming and swearing continued for some while until the first woman's voice eventually, slowly, subsided. Others followed. I checked that my door was still locked. This bedlam lasted for about ten minutes in total, but seemed so much longer.

It was terrifying. I wondered if one of the male wardens had, in fact, crept into that woman's cubicle, or whether she was psychotic, delusional, or as mad as a hatter.

I would never know. But what was becoming clearer to me was that there were many women in here who were helpless victims. Women for whom society had turned its back; whose lives had been wiped out, in all but their physicality. Women who had never been loved, or cared about. Who were once children who had never been loved or taken care of. They were casualties of our society, and denounced as having no value. Human lives which were felt fit only for the use, and profit, of others. These women knew nothing of tenderness, of happiness, and laughter. Thrown on a heap for the vultures to devour, their lives were bleaker than anyone could possibly imagine.

I was shaken by this whole experience.

More noise came crashing into the dormitory at seven o' clock. Starting at the beginning of the row, the intensity of the sound of banging grew louder and louder as a woman's raucous voice accompanied the use of some sort of object to rap on each door:

'*Get up!* Seven o' clock.' Bang! Bang! Bang! Then on the next door: '*Get up!* Seven o' clock.' Bang! Bang! Bang! Then the next: '*Get up!* Seven o' clock.' Bang! Bang! Bang! The noise became louder, and louder, until my door was similarly thrashed.

'Yes!' I shouted back, to let her know that I was up. Infrequently, I heard some of the other women responding with a weary moan, but most appeared not to answer.

The noises continued until every cubicle door had been attacked likewise. Occasionally the object would scrape across the door just before, or after, each crashing series of blows, seemingly dependent on the dexterity or lack of concentration of the worker, but all residents were left in no doubt as to the urgency of needing to get out of bed, and to vacate.

I could have slept for longer, but this wasn't The Ritz.

I needed to make use of every minute of the day, and so I pulled on some clothes and gathered all of my things together, except a small towel, and put everything else into my case which I shoved under the bed as far under as I could get it. It was important for me to hide my belongings to allow me enough time to get to the toilets and wash room before anyone had chance to look into my cubicle space. I couldn't lock the door from the outside.

As I came out of my cubicle I noticed that the female warden was talking to one of the resident women at the end of the gangway. She had her arms folded and was holding a battered old red shoe which I suspected had been her instrument for door bludgeoning.

When I passed her I glanced at her face. What sort of a person, I wondered, would want to work in a place like this? She had the sort of face which told me that she too had probably 'been around the block' a few times in her own life, and these sights and sounds around us were all just 'business as usual' for her.

Some of the women were beginning to emerge from their cubicles. Foot dragging, feeble-looking, expressionless faces, hunched shoulders and shabby clothes typified my co-residents. There were just a few who appeared to be more collected in their demeanour. It was impossible to imagine which of them had joined in last night's crazed chorus, but judging by the appearance of more of the women I witnessed as I walked to the wash room it could have included almost any one of them.

Just as I had imagined, there were no bathrooms, but just one long row of wash basins opposite a row of toilets. I presumed that Manchester City Council expected these inmates to use the public baths that were available in the city at that time, costing them an additional entrance fee that many of them simply wouldn't be able to afford. I managed to get in there early so that I could use the facilities before most of the other women. The thought of performing personal ablutions in front of an audience of queuing inmates would require the skills of a contortionist in order to retain any semblance of decorum, and I was in no fit state to put my levels of agility to the test right now. Besides, my towel was only the size of a small suitcase and my enlarged frame would require at least a king-sized bath towel.

I needn't have worried. Most of the women must have skipped a visit to the wash room. When I returned to my cubicle I was relieved to find that my case was exactly where I had left it. Some of the cubicle doors were still closed and I sensed that some of the women were still in bed. I presumed that there must follow another round of door-bashing to ensure that residents met with the deadline of eight-thirty to vacate their cubicles. I didn't plan to stick around to find out. I had a mission to pursue.

Out into the fresh air again, clutching my small suitcase, it felt so good to be out of that place. My first priority had to be to try to find something to eat that didn't stretch my limited budget! From my childhood treks across Manchester with my parents to catch the number ten bus, in nearby Greengate, I knew that there weren't any grocer's shops nearby, or even one of the newer self service stores which had started to appear in the nineteen-sixties. However, I remembered that there was an intriguing shop, only steps away from the cathedral, which sold special foods of various sorts. Today, it would be known as a delicatessen, or similar, but in those days it would have been regarded as a high-class, speciality food shop selling selected foods from the continent, and other, premium foodstuffs by appointment to The Crown.

I had to eat something, anything to satisfy my increasing appetite, and since that posh outlet was nearby I decided to take a peek inside.

In the shop, the smell of the cheeses and meats and fresh delicacies were almost too much for my taste buds to bear. I circled the stands of goods, checking the prices of items, having to remind myself of how little I could afford.

I left the shop with a rather smart brown paper bag with string handles inside of which the assistant had placed my two purchases. If I could manage to exercise enough self-restraint, I thought, these items might just serve as breakfast *and* mid-day meal: a simple bread product which we now know to be a half baguette, and a humble, circular box of Dairylea spread, with its individually wrapped soft cheeses. Hardly the high end of their stock, but I supposed that such common-place items as Dairylea spread could be a comparison against which their sales of the finest of French cheeses might score infinitely higher. And, anyway, they were delicious to me. Even if I couldn't spread the cheese without the use of a knife, I could place each on a chunk of the bread and swallow it almost whole, if necessary!

I could hardly wait to sample my purchases and quickly hastened my steps back to the cathedral grounds where I remembered having spotted a bench, overlooking a small landscaped area of lawn with a few ornamental trees. Much to my great disappointment, however, I turned a corner to find that an old tramp, with a beard as long as Methusaleh's, had settled himself, along with several shopping bags, on *my* chosen bench!

'Blow'! Barely ten minutes' before, the bench had been free. 'Where had *he* come from? Resigned, I knew that he had the same right to sit on the bench as I did. I walked towards a grassy bank, testing it first with my hand to check that it wasn't too damp with morning dew to sit down upon to eat my breakfast, picnic-style. Against the canopy of a trained, climbing wisteria I laid down my suitcase and sat for a moment, just taking in this tiny patch of nature's bounty within the swirling, unyielding city, as tiny speckles of pink petals fell around me.

My empty stomach brought me back to reality: I thought of my friend Jenny, with whom I had worked as a Saturday sales girl a few years' previously at the well-known city centre toy shop, Wiles', and what she used to say, when she was hungry: 'My stomach thinks my throat's been cut!' I almost giggled, thinking of her words, as I munched eagerly into a chunk of bread with a little triangle of soft cheese perched on top.

I missed Jenny. She had been a lovely friend. She had been brought up by loving, caring parents who had adopted her when she was a baby. They had told her about her adoption as soon as she had been old enough to understand. She had happily accepted her given status. She was an only child and it was evident from Jenny's calm, assured demeanour, and the close relationship which she shared, particularly with her mother, that

105

she felt secure, and loved. Jenny would never need to flee from *her* home, or ever be put into a hostel for the destitute in a grim part of town by her parents. She was prized too highly for that ever to happen.

It would have been good to tell her of my present difficulties. To hear her voice, and for her to know how much I was struggling right now. I resolved that, as soon as I could find somewhere to live, I would write to her and tell her that I was expecting a baby.

Hunger satisfied, I wrapped and carefully placed the rest of my half baguette and three cheeses, into the paper carrier bag. I suddenly became conscious that to picnic on the hallowed, high grounds of the cathedral, in full view of people rushing to-and-from their way to work, might look more than a bit odd. I stood up to shake the flaky crumbs and petals from my clothes, then gathered together my case and other belongings.

Glancing behind me at the cathedral, I had an impulsive idea that, since it represented one of the highest of religious institutions, it might be worth exploring whether the Vicar, or Dean, or whoever was in charge this morning could help me.

My loose plan of action was to see if I could find a convent in the city where the nuns might be able to help me in this difficult situation, rather like the one in London. However, since I was outside such an esteemed place of worship it was worth giving it a try in here first.

Hesitantly, I walked into the north entrance of the cathedral and into the nave where there were some rows of chairs. I sat down at the end of one row, trying not to feel intimidated by the six hundred years of history of this sacred space; its stained glass, its wings, and the magnificence of the floor-to-ceiling organ. The sheer scale of the building was a far cry from Edge Lane Methodist church in Droylsden, with its chatty, welcoming congregation where I had gone to Sunday School and church services as a child.

I was suddenly gripped by my sense of 'aloneness' in this vast, glorious space. I had not been blessed with the sort of upbringing which inspired confidence, or any sense of self-importance. Quite the contrary. As a child, my father would frequently insist that 'children should be seen and not heard,' and I learned that having a sense of modesty at all times was everything. In addition, social expectations of people in general were such that we kept quiet about our personal business. With my 'baby business' speaking for itself I felt anxious about being judged harshly, or even of being misjudged to be 'penitent', such was the social stigma of unmarried motherhood.

I caught sight of a robed cleric moving around, further ahead in the cathedral. He seemed to be attending to something, and I couldn't quite see what. I suddenly felt unnerved by the prospect of him noticing me, a lone young woman, pregnant and carrying a suitcase. Furthermore, I couldn't imagine that someone so venerated, in such high office, would be able to advise me about anything so practical as to where I could stay. And would he judge me as a 'woman who had fallen from grace'? He probably didn't even know what help might be available in Manchester, let alone how to begin to address such a practicality, I decided.

What am I doing in here? I had talked myself out of the idea.

Grabbing my suitcase I made for the door again. I had to find another way of asking clergy for help, I thought. Maybe trying to seek out some nuns who may be more approachable might be a better idea.

I began to wander in the direction of Deansgate in the city centre, with which I became familiar as a child during family trips and, later, working in Manchester. There must be some convents, of any denomination, where I might be able to undertake some sort of domestic work in exchange for bed and board, as I had done in London.

This was my only hope. I was gripped by the fear of having to sleep under the stars again, this time on my own and just weeks' away from giving birth. I had only enough money to cover one more night at the hostel, and a few more shillings left over to get something to eat this evening.

I trudged slowly up Market Street, one of the main shopping thoroughfares in the city, and eventually arrived at Piccadilly Gardens where I knew that I could sit down for a while and try to work out how I could obtain the information I needed. It was no good trying to ask anyone. What sort of a crazy question would that be:

'Excuse me but, do you know of any convents in the city?' It was evident that I wasn't looking to become a nun.

People were moving through the gardens en route to their destinations. It was a beautiful day in late July. Some other people appeared simply to want to sit for a while, and watch the 'world go by', whilst others were opening lunch boxes, eating sandwiches and snacks as the pigeons descended, hopeful of scavenging any crumbs they could find.

There was no one around like me, though, with a suitcase.

I looked round for a telephone box. I spotted a red box not far away.

Inside the phone box was a telephone directory and a copy of the Yellow Pages. I was pleased that I could try to search for the information I needed. It was either that or, as a last resort, I could telephone the Samaritans.

I found a listing called: 'The Presentation Convent'. I rang the number. The telephone was answered by a kindly-sounding nun, who introduced herself as Sister Dorothea. She listened quietly as I nervously poured out my story, asking her if she could help me. No longer was I pretending to be married. There was no point at this stage, since I was clearly alone; I couldn't tell anything now but the truth. Feeling desperate again, I found myself on the verge of tears.

'Now, Susan, we work primarily with the elderly, and unfortunately we have neither any staff vacancies nor a spare room available at present, otherwise we would be able to offer you some help with this,' she explained. Then she paused for a moment. 'Now let me see, though, I think there's a convent which is located out of town, called St. Joseph's where, given its history, you might be able to find some help.'

I thanked her. It was, at least, a lifeline that I could try.

After looking up the number of St. Joseph's convent in the Victoria Park area I tried for a second time. A young, female voice answered, which I supposed might be that of a novice. Once again, I explained that I was in a terrible mess: I was expecting a baby, I had nowhere to go; nowhere to sleep. There was a moment of silence on the telephone line. How shocking this must have sounded to a protected, chaste young woman who was preparing for a life of relative seclusion.

'Can you manage to get to Anson Road, in Victoria Park?' she asked, followed quickly by: 'tomorrow would be preferable, because Sister Augustine will be back from attending a conference at Salford University, and she's the best person to help you.'

'Yes, I can come tomorrow, Sister.' Then, gauging how long it might take me to get there I suggested, 'It will probably be around mid-to-late morning, if that's convenient?'

'I'll tell Sister Augustine this evening. We'll see you tomorrow, Susan.'

'Thank you, Sister. That's very kind of you.'

As I placed the receiver down on the telephone, I sobbed with the release of pent-up anxiety; of great relief in at last finding a glimmer of hope amidst a sea of hopelessness. I pulled out a long piece of toilet paper from my bag to wipe my face dry, courtesy of the last-chance saloon in town, aka the hostel on Long Mill-gate, where I would have to stay another night.

Out of the stuffy telephone box, I put my face up to the sun and, feeling much better than before, I headed back to Piccadilly gardens to eat my leftover piece of bread, and three last triangles of soft cheese.

Sitting in the sunshine, now with a little time to relax, I counted out my money. I put aside six shillings for a bed at the hostel for tonight; I worked out that the miserably small sum I had remaining might just buy me a bag of chips for my evening meal, *and* possibly also the bus fare to Victoria Park tomorrow. If it wasn't enough then I would have to walk it.

If only I could borrow, or get hold of, some money from somewhere. I knew that I wouldn't be eligible to apply for Social Security benefits of any kind without a fixed address. I suddenly remembered an embarrassing and humiliating experience in relation to claiming state benefits. My thoughts harked back to a dreadful period at home.

It was when I had begun to study for my O' Levels, having experienced over a year of my father's bullying, violent behaviour towards me. Throughout this awful time he had deliberately refused to speak to me, except only for the occasions in which he issued stern directives:

'Go and wash the pots.' 'Go to bed.' Do this, do that, he would say, angrily, and in hostile tones.

The change in my father's attitude towards me seemed to stem from the time of the run up to my O' Level examinations. In 1966 we were the first year to study for the new CSE examinations, alongside our GCE's.

As part of the Geography course our teacher announced, in the autumn before the examinations, that we would be expected to undertake a week's field study course which would entail staying in a youth hostel in the Peak District. We would study the villages in the area, the countryside, and local resources. Upon our return to school, we would submit a thesis, the mark of which would contribute to our overall assessment.

Choosing carefully an appropriate moment when both my parents were present, and one well in advance of the actual time of the intended study, I nervously broached the subject of the field study visit. It was met with a subdued response from my mother, who knew how this news would be received by my father. Dad said nothing, and glared into his newspaper.

He would normally have flatly rejected outright any idea which involved my absence from home. But, because it was a prerequisite of an important examination, for the very first time he withheld judgement. He must have felt that if he responded to the idea with a blanket refusal his objection would be perceived at school to be unreasonable, and jeopardizing my chances of academic success.

The forthcoming trip, which would place me beyond the reaches of his control, seemed to threaten his jurisdiction. It overruled his true wishes and I was convinced, with everything that followed, that he was determined to make me pay for it.

This terrible time in my home life spelled a deeply harrowing period for me in which my father's ostracism of me was not only unwarranted but cruel, and it became increasingly untenable for me to continue to live at home. His behaviour towards me was something that was never discussed. My older sister Jean and I had never dared to question my father's actions. I felt that I simply had to try, somehow, to reach the end of the school year to fulfil all my examination requirements.

My father became increasingly violent towards me. If I went out in the evening to spend time with a few friends he insisted that I was back home by the dot of ten o' clock, and *not a minute* later. I would jump off the bus in Droylsden and run as fast as I could up Dawlish Avenue, then down Buckingham Road in a state of sheer panic to try to make my ten o' clock deadline. Invariably I would fall foul of the deadline, sometimes only by minutes, but never more than six minutes' later. The fact that this was, arguably, only a *mild* transgression didn't matter to my father. If I was only *one* minute late I had to suffer the same consequences. I was met with a stony-faced, angry parent who had geared himself up to do what he minded to do.

It was the same routine every time: as I apologised profusely I was first subjected to an angry, abusive rant about having broken his stipulation. This was followed by his moving towards me menacingly, as I fearfully backed away towards the door leading to our front room, the stairs, and my bedroom. I was forced to listen, because the demi-god was speaking. There could be no exchange. No excuses in the world could justify having broken his dictate. Then, always:

Bang! Hitting my face so hard, he deliberately banged my head against the door. This was followed by another, and another. Tears dripped down my face. He would bawl at me.

'And you can stop that snivelling. *Now!*'

My streaming eyes looked at him with the hatred I now felt, and he knew it. As soon as he had decided that he had delivered enough punishment, that I was hurting enough, he told me to go up to bed. Misery. Absolute misery. He was an angry, five foot ten inches tall, strong male, and I was a sixteen, then seventeen year old, five foot female. Every time I cried myself to sleep, and vowed to break free from under his control as soon as I could.

I never dared to speak about any of the issues, such was my father's attitude in relation to parental discipline; his view that offspring should never question or oppose what a parent deems to be appropriate for them. Furthermore I feared having to suffer a greater escalation of retributive violence, so I kept quiet. My way of dealing with the whole, seemingly eternal business was to pretend outwardly that I was fine, and that all was well, ostensibly ignoring the ostracism and the brutality. But deep down inside, I hurt. I was distressed every single day. I was captive to his loathsome ways. This was not the way a parent should treat a daughter, and I knew that this was far from a normal existence. I feigned a veneer of acquiescence in day-to day issues, whilst privately despising my father's very being, knowing that one day I would be able to escape.

I had desperately wanted to be a teacher, and this meant studying for A' Levels and, therefore, in a state of great uncertainty as to whether I would be able to complete the courses due to my home life, I embarked upon my sixth form study. Increasingly, however, the need to leave home became more important to me than having any hope of an interesting career.

I planned my departure in great detail. I mentioned to my parents, almost nonchalantly at first, that I felt that I really would be better off in a job, with the possibility of returning to study at some time in the near future, on a part-time basis. Some weeks later, I informed them that I was going to see my Headmistress, with a view to leaving school at the end of my first term in the Lower Sixth. In reality, I told the Headmistress that life was so intolerable for me at home, due to my father's ostracism of me, his bullying ways and the violence which he inflicted upon me; that I had no option but to give up my studies in order to get a job, and then leave home. She was very sympathetic, but in those days teachers, along with social workers and the police, rarely sought to intervene in domestic matters. She commiserated that I was experiencing such difficulties and understood my reasons for needing to leave school. She wished me well for the future.

The whole thrust of my existence became consumed with the need to get away.

My Guardian Angel must have worked her wonderful deed: before leaving school I applied for a job as a Clerical Assistant at The Sun Alliance Insurance Company in the centre of Manchester, and about a week later I was offered the position in writing, with a start date of Monday 16th January.

Unfortunately, however, my Angel was unable to fix *everything*.

Having left school just before Christmas in nineteen sixty-six, aged seventeen years old, Dad sternly announced that, since I had left school, and despite the fact that I was going to start full-time work in mid-January I now had to justify my 'keep'. He told me to go to the local Social Security office in the new year and register as unemployed for two weeks in order to make a claim for benefits.

I knew that any 'costs' related to my bed and board could be met by household income as before but, as usual, Dad was being deliberately unkind towards me, making me pay for having independently taken matters into my own hands, with no involvement from him in my decision. Because he generally refused to speak to me anyway he was hoist with his own petard. I had therefore managed to pull this off under his nose, making the likelihood of further decisions possible which would enable me to break free from his parental control.

I made my way to the benefits office and took my place in the queue. When I reached the desk it was necessary to explain the situation to a middle-aged, female member of staff, who thought my application to be unjustified. She brought the Manager to listen to my repeated explanation. I felt no sense of betrayal towards my father in telling them that he had insisted upon my making a claim for benefits.

'But you have been offered a job,' she said incredulously. *'It's a wait only of just two weeks!'*

'Yes, I know,' I replied, squirming in my shoes, 'but my father insists that I bring in some money to pay for my keep.'

Both women threw each other a 'look' over their respective sets of spectacles; looks that spoke volumes.

After an hour of waiting I was called to the desk and informed that I would be paid two pounds per week for each of the two weeks.

When I received my giro cheques I duly went to the post office to draw each, and handed over the respective amounts to my mother, as Dad had instructed me to do.

I found the whole incident of being made suddenly to have to account for the absence of two weeks' income only, whilst living at home, to be a shaming and humiliating experience, exactly as my father had intended it. Moreover I would have been prepared to pay my mother retrospectively, in staggered payments to make up for those two weeks, beginning with receipt of my first pay packet, but my father insisted on immediate recompense. It was testimony that I was living in a house filled with abject misery. A house where malevolence towards me would never end until I packed my bags and left home.

Sitting in that July sunshine in Piccadilly gardens, I recalled vividly the private hell of it all. I was adamant that no child of mine will ever be treated so unkindly, and nor will I ever allow anyone else to treat them so. If need be, I'll fight with every bone in my body to give my baby, and any other children I may have in the future, the very best life that's within my power to provide.

I sat for a while, turning my attention to this small niche of the city's central, well-known garden. It was filled with flowers of every colour, and its beauty and scent flooded my senses with the pleasure and hope that I needed. At last, there appeared to be a chance of a breakthrough for the better in my fortunes.

Now I could afford to take the afternoon more slowly. The last thing I wanted to do was to arrive too early at the dreaded hostel.

I sauntered towards the bus station which was located to the rear of the gardens, and poked my head into the tiny office where the bus inspector was usually to be found.

'I wonder if you could tell me please, where I will be able to catch a bus tomorrow for Victoria Park?'

An older man with a handle-bar moustache pointed to further down the station.

'You see that lady up there with the large blue bag? Well just past there is the stand for number twenty three, and way further up where you can see those children playing is the number fifty that will also take you to Victoria Park.

I could see that a twenty three was stationed there presently, and so I walked up to the bus and approached the driver to enquire about the cost of the fare for my journey the next day. I was in luck! Unless, later on, my portion of chips was going to be prohibitively expensive, I worked out that I should be able to travel by bus the next day and not have to face the potentially long, tiring walk out of town to my destination! Hallelujah!

'Thank you, Angel,' I whispered.

I began to retrace my steps back towards the insalubrious part of town where I would have to end the day. After browsing in Lewis's store at its range of beautiful maternity wear, I ambled down Market Street towards the historic Shambles area where I knew there was a fish and chip shop. Thankfully, I found a nearby bench and managed to kill some more time eating what was effectively my last meal of the day, before having to face the squalid hostel. Already, groups of people were trickling into the area, many of whom I was sure would probably be going for a meal in a restaurant and enjoying a few drinks during the evening.

It was time for me to book a bed for the night.

I was given the very same cubicle in which I had spent the previous night: there was no mistaking that exact view of the alleyway through the barred window, and I recognised the particular stains and tarnishes on the table by the window. I decided that the best thing for me would be to try to get as much sleep as I could. Tomorrow was going to be another trying day when I would need every ounce of stamina I could summon.

Lying in that creaky bed, I sensed that I was the first female to book a bed in this dormitory for the night, since the *whole place* seemed quiet. I reflected upon the previous evening when it had been equally quiet for quite a while after Dad had left me. Then, much later on at around midnight, and in the early hours of the morning, I heard the warden's keys jangling, and many doors banging, as women came to their beds.

In a flash of insight, it occurred to me *why* these lost-looking souls came to bed so late! They were streetwalkers, *of course*! Maybe not all of them, I thought, but I was sure that most of those women had spent, if perhaps not *all* day, most of the evening selling their bodies for sex in return for cash. They would be risking their safety as they ambled around this unsavoury part of the city, being taken up alleyways and also into the cars of kerb-crawlers.

I had witnessed similar incidences of this in Piccadilly in the past when a small group of my friends and I had passed through on our way to catching our buses, and we noticed car after car stopping while the drivers weighed up the prostitutes in their respective patches, and solicited:

'Hey, how much?'

The sorts of women who stayed in this hostel were, I felt, far more unfortunate individuals than those, and for whom there was no escape. They didn't have the means to try to carve out an independent life. They would be targeted by unscrupulous men who made *their* living off the backs of women who had been released from the asylums and other, similar institutions.

I remembered that in my early teenage years I was vaguely aware that there were national initiatives to release many people from Asylums who were judged not to be a danger to themselves or others. During this period in the early nineteen sixties lay the intention to care for people with mental health conditions more compassionately within the community. However, many of those released 'slipped through the net' as successive governments failed to keep pace with need in providing timely and appropriate care, or supported living provision within our society.

They suffered greatly due to a lack of appropriate housing and mental health support. They weren't equipped to look after themselves. Moreover, it's not difficult to envisage how women especially would immediately fall prey to exploitative relationships. This hostel, I deduced, and possibly many others like it, was testimony to the failures of a movement which was originally intended as humanitarian, and serving a public and moral necessity but, in practice, plunged many vulnerable women into harm's way.

It was highly likely, I mused, that the women staying at this hostel had pimps who would be waiting for them at an agreed place and hour, to take all their earnings in exchange for the cost of their bed and a small amount to feed them the following day.

Such streetwalkers were not the sort of prostitutes who wore makeup, mascara and bright red lipstick. Not for them, either, tight clothing, low-cut tops and six inch stilettos. Their insignia was poverty, unwashed hair, and shoes which were falling off their feet; their looks alone sometimes indicated serious mental health disorders, women who had been caught in the unforgiving net of ruthless exploitation. They stood on the last rung of the human ladder; whose sex fees were low enough to attract the most unsavoury male sections of society, that is if they managed to get paid at all. What was worse, was the idea that most of these women wouldn't even know about STD clinics or have the temerity to visit them.

My second night in the hostel for destitute women played out as it had in the evening before. I fell asleep relatively early, to be woken by the noises of repeated footsteps, keys jangling and heavy metal doors banging shut late at night, and in the early hours of the morning. I heard mutterings, moaning, and conversations with themselves, long after the warden had walked away. This time, however, there appeared to be no middle-of-the-night bedlam; no raucous yelling or hysteria; no mass crescendo of fear, for which I felt relieved, because it must have been as frightening for some of the others as it had been for me.

I awoke before the warden had chance to clatter on my door, glad to have the night behind me, and hoping never again to have to resort to sleeping in such an outmoded and heartless institution. Within these walls I had experienced a glimpse of life in one of the most desperate and sordid pockets of the city unimaginable, and forever deeply etched into my memory.

CHAPTER 7

In the nineteen-sixties Victoria Park had all the appearances of a vast, landscaped area. It was a few miles south of the city, and on one side of the main road there were large, grand, Victorian residences, and on the other was a green expanse including that of a large public park. The whole area was leafy and lush in vegetation, and a far cry from where I had stayed for the last few nights.

Buses had bus conductors who took your fare, frequently assisted with luggage and children's trolleys, or pushchairs, and who would shout out the name of an area as it was approached. I had already asked the conductor if he would kindly let me know when we came to Anson Road and, as we did, I spotted what I thought might be the convent, as the bus hurtled past.

Alighting the bus carefully, carrying my suitcase and my shoulder bag, I walked back down the road towards the large residence that I thought may be that of St Joseph's. A lady who was walking her dog was about to pass me.

'Excuse me, please, but could you tell me if that building further down there is a Roman Catholic convent called St. Joseph's?' I asked, pointing to the property in question.

'I'm not sure what it's called,' she said, 'but you might be right, because we do see nuns going in and out of there.'

I thanked her, and walked on towards the building. It was a large, Victorian house, set near the edge of the main road in its own extensive grounds. I entered through a gate opposite the main door. The house was surrounded by a host of established trees, climbers and flower-filled borders.

I was nervous. How would they judge me? There was so much at stake in this appointment.

I lifted the beautiful heavy brass knocker on the front door and brought it down hard a few times. Seconds later the large imposing door opened.

'You must be Susan?' The novice was expecting me, and invited me into the spacious hallway. 'Please take a seat here,' she said, 'and I'll go and find Sister Augustine for you.' I was glad not to have to carry my case for a few minutes, and I warmed to the welcoming smile of the young nun. The greeting marked a stark contrast with that of the warden in the hostel in Long Millgate. My baby seemed to appreciate it also as she or he thrashed around, quite vigorously within me.

Barely three minutes later, an elderly nun in full black habit appeared and walked towards me. She held her outstretched hand to shake mine.

'Good morning, Susan. I'm Sister Augustine.' She smiled. 'Please come through here, and sit down.' She led me into an adjoining room and sat behind a beautiful old desk.

'I understand that you are in need of some assistance, Susan,' she said, inviting me to sit down opposite her. Sitting on the edge of my seat, I felt that I had nothing else to lose now, but to summarize to her the whole sorry story.

I outlined some of the difficulties of my home life, and my need to move out; meeting someone with whom I became pregnant, and who had treated me badly in London; my return to Manchester and having only pennies left in my purse now, with nowhere to sleep. I was too ashamed, however, to tell her of my father's involvement in putting me into the hostel for destitute women.

Why was I protecting Dad's actions; his role in what I felt was an act of ruthlessness? I couldn't bring myself to tell of that awfulness. What parent puts his under age daughter who is heavily pregnant in such an institution, knowing she has little money left and couldn't pay for more than a few night's safety?

I didn't want her to know that I came from such a heartless parent. I was still having difficulties in coming to terms with what my father had recently done.

I needn't have worried, because Sister Augustine seemed to want to help me, irrespective of how I had found my way to her door. Thank goodness. And, yes, there *was* some goodness in the world, after all. I was *so* relieved.

The nun led me through the convent to the back door, and outside to where her car was parked.

'It's only a short drive away, Susan,' she said, in her gentle Irish brogue. 'This is just an interim measure,' she said, 'until you have your baby.'

I didn't give her comment another thought. When you are in such a dire situation your only concern lies in the immediacy of that moment and, in this instance, in resolving the problem of where I could sleep, and how I was going to eat. This nun was prepared to offer me a bed! I thanked her profoundly.

Sister Augustine introduced me to a nun called Sister Mary, who was the resident nun in the Staff House where I would be staying, in the grounds of St Joseph's Roman Catholic High School for Girls.

I was led to a really lovely, comfortable room, which over-looked the garden. Sister Mary said that I could have the rest of the day free in which to settle, and the next day I should report to her and she would introduce me to the nun in charge of the kitchens, where I would be expected to undertake some work.

In the meantime she took me to a refectory-cum-dining area and offered me a seat, while she went in search of some food for me to eat. I felt overwhelmed by the generosity of these nuns, for taking me in and offering me a sanctuary, a safe place to be, and for offering me food also. I remembered the books of parables I had read as a child; the stories Jesus had told about 'helping thy neighbour', and offering food and shelter to those in need. This kindness was being bestowed to me on the grounds of pure faith and pure goodness and they didn't know me. It put my parents to shame, I thought.

The new day dawned. I woke early. There were movements in the house, and I supposed that the nuns present would have been rising early to go to prayer. In addition I was aware that there were other staff in the house who worked for the Sisters, engaged in domestic chores of various sorts.

I was keen to make a good start, and so I got washed and dressed and reported to Sister Mary, as agreed.

I had never seen such a vast kitchen, with many ovens, surface areas, sinks, and aluminium shelving and racks, far more impressive than that of the Domestic Science kitchens I had been used to at school. This area provided hundreds of daily, hot cooked meals at lunchtime for a whole school of girls. There seemed to be several women working in it, all headed by one nun, Sister Brigitte.

A small number of breakfasts were made daily for the nuns and resident staff, before the team sprang into action making a full dinner and pudding for the pupils at mid-day. After that, at tea time, a light supper was made for the nuns and the resident staff, and the next day it would all begin again, ad infinitum. The weekends provided a respite from having to make the bulk of dinners, since there were no pupils in school, and a skeleton staff was required to make only the nuns' and resident staff' meals.

Being part of such a huge catering provision was a steep learning curve for me. It was hard, physical work. Unlike my role in the London convent, where I was allocated a particular role with a clearly defined area of responsibility, I became a 'moveable feast', required to fill in and adapt to a rapidly changing array of jobs, wherever additional help was required. One day I would be given vegetable preparation, another day I might be moved into meats, pudding prep, washing up, or simply cleaning surfaces. It was entirely up to the supervisor, Janice.

I liked Jan. She was about thirty years' old, hard working and with a great sense of humour, which had us all reeling with laughter, but it only surfaced when Sister Brigitte wasn't around. Jan was Sister Brigitte's right hand woman, and therefore even light-hearted humour was strictly off limits during productive periods.

To give Sister Brigitte credit too, I saw in her a nun who worked extremely physically hard. Her attire was adapted to suit the hot working conditions of a busy kitchen. She would invariably wear her sleeves rolled up beyond her elbows, and quite frequently I would see her bring up her long white apron to mop her brow. She had also been granted exemption to wearing the full veil which all the other nuns wore, covering her head only in a small cap; her veil and neckerchief reserved for wearing elsewhere, other than in the kitchen. I respected her for her dedication since no wage would be paid and her days demanded the utmost stamina. She planned all of the meals, ordered all the required supplies and worked physically hard to ensure that hundreds of mouths were fed nutritiously by the early afternoon. I wondered whether, in devoting her life to God, she had also signed up to her gruelling work schedule in the kitchen also.

On my first Sunday there, during which there was only light work to do, we were ahead in our jobs and Jan asked me if I would like a cup of tea and a sit down before finishing off the chores for the end of the day.

She was a good woman. She smiled a lot, and seemed happy working for the Sisters.

'I was once like you,' she said to me.

'What do you mean, Jan?'

'I come from Preston,' she said proudly. 'I was full of dreams. I was madly in love with my boyfriend, Mark. We'd known each other for almost two years, first as friends, and then we became closer. I was a good Catholic girl. I always went to church, just as my parents always had. Anyway, at eighteen I became pregnant. I told Mark, and he just couldn't cope with it. He finished with me. I didn't know what to do. Anyway, I plucked up the courage to tell my parents, and they just hit the roof!'

'You were very brave to tell your parents, Jan. My parents were the last people I told.'

'Brave, maybe, but foolish too, thinking that they would actually help me,' she said.

We sipped away at our tea, and I immediately felt an affinity with this woman sitting in front of me, as she continued her tale.

'They insisted that I go away to have my baby, and told no one else. They found St Joseph's convent, here in Victoria Park. At one time the convent was a Home run by the nuns for unmarried mothers. This changed a few years ago as other, similar institutions had better provision, and also because many of the nuns were older and there was a rise in the number of pregnant girls and young women. Years before that, many of the girls had been in service, impregnated by the masters of the house, or their sons, and when they came here they were called 'penitents' and taught how to live more 'chaste' lives alongside the Sisters, after their babies had been given up for adoption.'

Now, I understood why Sister Augustine had seemed to be so accepting of my situation.

'So, Jan, what happened? What of your baby?'

Jan's eyes became wet with tears, as she looked down into her cup. She was quiet for a moment, then began again: 'She was a darling baby. I called her Rachael. She had lots of curly dark hair, just like me. She was a smiler, a gorgeous little ray of sunshine. I loved her and cared for her for two months. Then the nuns said that it would be better, all round, if I had her adopted. That way, she would have two parents, instead of one; parents who could give her everything I couldn't. They said that I could start out all over again and one day have a normal life. I didn't care about my life. What's normal anyway? But I knew that I would never be able to properly provide for her, or give her the sort of life she deserved. I couldn't even afford, or manage, to live independently. And what sort of a life would it have been for her here, surrounded by women wearing habits and veils, and rarely seeing any men? And so I gave her up to be adopted. I felt, and still do, that I betrayed her, my own flesh and blood.' She added, 'I hope that one day she'll come to forgive me.'

Jan wiped her eyes. I felt desperately sad for her, and for her loss. She reached into her bag and pulled out a photograph of her beautiful, happy baby girl to show me.

'There isn't a day goes by when I don't think of her. She'll be eleven years' old at the end of this month.'

I tried to offer words of consolation but they seemed meaningless in the face of the great sadness which she had carried all those years.

'So, did you return home?' I enquired.

'I sensed that I was no longer wanted. I had brought shame to my Mum and Dad, and to those in our family who knew the truth. I seriously thought about it but I knew, deep down, having had such a life-changing experience, that I needed to just keep going. As it happened, the nuns here at St Joseph's School were looking for additional paid help, and the job came with a room, and so I've been here ever since,' she said with a smile.

'And just before Christmas last year I met a wonderful man called Tony. He works for a firm based in Cheshire that supplies a lot of the foodstuffs for the school. He knows about Rachael.'

I watched her face light up again as she talked about Tony. She said that she was hoping that he might ask her to marry him, but it was still 'early days' yet. Jan radiated a happiness, despite her years of sadness at having lost her precious baby.

'Not many men want someone who's had a child. He's not like that. He says that he loves me.' She changed the subject: 'Now, what about you? Are you going to marry the father?' she asked.

I told Jan about my experiences in London.

'Look,' she said, trying to consider my options, 'he probably deeply regrets behaving the way he did. Why not give him a second chance? Remember, it's *his baby too*. The father of *my* baby just didn't want to know. It sounds like your fellow was looking forward to having a family. *I* just didn't have a choice.'

Later in the evening I sat on top of my bed in my cosy room overlooking the garden, thinking about what Jan had said. Was I supposed to feel grateful that Sean had actually wanted this child? *That*, at the expense of my own well being? Surely, it's only reasonable to expect both sets of reassurances, that the father of one's child cares enough about you to want to keep you safe and well, as much as his own child?

I still felt aggrieved about Sean's treatment of me. What he did was inexcusable. Also, in this era of shot-gun weddings are we so blind as to think only about obviating the matter of illegitimacy, and not the viability of a long-term union between two people who happened to have engaged in sex outside marriage?

It seemed to me that when a young, single woman becomes pregnant the idea of getting married was the first thought that springs to mind for many people. A quick panacea. Sorted. What comes later doesn't matter, so long as we sweep away the problem *now* with a quick fix.

Though I liked Jan very much, she was suggesting, like many other people would, that I should be grateful for having a boyfriend who seems to be interested in the forthcoming arrival of his child. And implying, also perhaps, that it was possible to make such a marriage 'work', since there is a unifying common factor, that of our child. My father had also raised the option of marriage. Interestingly he too hadn't asked me if I *wanted* to marry Sean, or how *I* felt about the prospect. My wishes hadn't entered into it.

However, the matter that Jan had to say about remembering that Sean was the father of this child was something that struck a reasonable chord within me. I conceded that if he wanted to take an active role in our child's upbringing that would be something that I should consider. However, knowing Sean's restlessness I couldn't imagine how this might play out. My conscience was slowly telling me that he should have the opportunity to see his own child. Importantly, also, I felt that he should contribute towards this baby's upkeep. I wasn't sure how that could happen either, though, because his work record was highly unpredictable, as he flitted from place to place and seemed to find it hard to settle anywhere.

It was with some reservation, that same evening, that I decided to make renewed contact with Sean, to let him know where I was living at the present time.

Without any more ado I scribbled a brief note, informing him of where I was, and reminding him when the baby was due. I decided that I would post it the next day, using a stamp which Jan had given to me, and send it to the address in Notting Hill Gate, where I assumed that he was still living.

Life at St Joseph's Roman Catholic High School for Girls continued happily from day to day, as my pregnancy reached the end of its eighth month. I was still working as hard as I could in the kitchens and, as a result, I would often fall asleep shortly after my day's shift had ended, after having eaten my supper. Above all else, though, I counted myself as being blessed in having been given a roof over my head, and nourishing food to eat each day. There were always, of course, nagging doubts about where all this was leading to; I had vague notions about the possibilities of finding some sort of residential work where I might be allowed to take care of my baby. That's as far as I had time to hope for, because the sheer experience of carrying a child whilst working hard each day, and interacting with fellow workers, consumed all of my energy.

I missed having a little money to spend. I needed to buy some personal items and I didn't want to ask the Sisters for money.

Jan was very kind. She offered to buy me some things, but I knew that she wouldn't be earning a good wage and I couldn't bring myself to take her up on her offer.

I also missed contact with 'the outside world'. I had no idea what was happening in the world, or even in *this* country. I had no access to a radio or television, and I had no money for a newspaper. It was a strange feeling, that of being completely annexed from society, yet living only a short distance from one of the largest cities in the country.

Importantly also, no one knew where I was, other than Sean, and though I was surrounded by all the staff and nuns who worked at the school, I was feeling increasingly lonely, and very much alone in my pregnancy.

My mother had never really been able to talk easily about women's issues, but I missed having contact with Mum, and at eighteen years old I would have valued her advice on my pregnancy and what I might expect. I only had the textbook versions to inform me of what would very soon be a major event in my life.

I made the decision to telephone St Mary's Maternity Hospital in central Manchester where I had attended a pre-natal clinic in the early stages of my pregnancy. A new appointment was arranged for me for the following week, and I decided that I would pluck up the courage to speak to Sister Brigitte about it the following day. I needed to be granted leave of absence to attend the clinic and I also wanted to ask her if it might be possible to find a small amount of money for my bus fare.

That evening, feeling tired as usual, I drew the curtains across the full length windows overlooking the beautiful gardens of the school. I clambered into bed, feeling that I had made some progress during the day in re-establishing my antenatal appointments. I needed the assurance of knowing that everything was progressing as it should be, with my baby developing healthily, since my due date was only a matter of around four weeks away.

I had spent a long day of hard work, scrubbing and scouring enormous pots and pans, and then washing floors and walls until they gleamed. I was asleep within a few minutes of getting into bed.

It was almost midnight when I was suddenly awoken. There was a frantic rapping on the French windows of my room. Startled, I wondered if I had dreamt the noise. It began again. I slipped out of bed to peer between the heavy curtains into the moonlit garden. There, in the dim light, was the face of Sean pressed against the glass, begging to be let in.

He was coughing, and spluttering in the cold night air, looking quite unwell, having arrived by National Express coach from London that evening in a bid to find me.

I opened the French windows and he hurtled inside, flinging his arms around me, and coughing simultaneously.

'Sue, my darling, Sue! I have missed you so much; I am so sorry for treating you badly, and I love you, and our baby.' He hugged me close to him.

'Sean, you're unwell. What are you doing, travelling here to find me when you're so poorly? It sounds like you have bronchitis again.' As an afterthought, I wanted him to know that it wasn't wise to want to get back together again:

'Look, I can't cope, Sean, with your drinking, and your jealousy. Things get out of hand.'

'I promise never to hurt you again. I just want us to be happy, and for us to love our baby, and be together.'

They were heartfelt words, but I knew Sean so well; his intentions were always well meant, but he never seemed to be able to live up to them.

'Anyway, what are you doing here? How did you find me?'

'Your description of the school and its grounds, and this staff house. It wasn't too hard. I'm just so happy to be here with you. I wanted to tell you how much I love you. Can I stay here with you for a few days? I don't have anywhere to stay right now.'

With that, he started coughing again, and I realised how ill he really was. I agreed to his staying the night, but on condition that he would have to leave very early in the morning before anyone could catch sight of him. He hugged me again, and planted several kisses on my face, before undressing and climbing into the narrow, single bed. How the two of us managed to fit into the bed, back-to-back, with my swollen belly protruding outwards towards the door, I will never know.

Sean's coughing fits continued throughout the night, disturbing both of us. He sipped at water, then threw the covers over his head to try to quell the sounds of his raucous outbursts.

I hadn't realised it, but his coughs had shaken the very walls of the whole house.

At early light, the door of my room was unlocked abruptly from the outside with a master key, and the door was flung wide open.

There stood the figure of Sister Mary.

'*Susan!*' she proclaimed in horror, 'Have you a *MAN* in your bed?'

I shot up, bolt upright, clinging to the bed covers, whilst my accomplice immediately threw the same over his sweaty, sickly head.

'Oh, Sister Mary. I'm sorry. I'm so sorry,' I whimpered.' I was just about to explain, when she turned on the spot, and in loud howls of shock and retribution she exclaimed:

'*Just wait until Mother Superior hears about this!*' Then she was gone.

Well that's it, I decided immediately. There was nothing else for it! I scrambled out of bed, as Sean emerged from underneath the covers.

'Shit!' he said, then: 'What are you doing?'

'I'm going. I'm not waiting around here for Mother Superior to show up and have me answer to some crime I haven't committed; and for her to dispense some sort of punishment when all I did was to let you in when you had nowhere to go; and were so sick!'

Sean joined my scramble. I grabbed everything I had and stuffed it all back into my trusty suitcase, threw on my clothes in great haste and made my way out of the room, for good. Straightening his tie, Sean shouted after me:

'For God's sake, Sue, where are you going?'

I kept going. I knew that, despite having been working in London, Sean would have no money; I knew that he wouldn't be able to help me out of this one. I had to try to help myself again out of this new calamity, somehow.

'I'm going to St Joseph's Convent,' I shouted back to him, as I stepped out of the French windows into the grounds. 'I'm going to ask Sister Augustine if she'll help me again. I have no-one to turn to, but her.'

I walked as fast as my load would allow, through the grounds to the main road.

I turned in the direction of the city, still feeling bleary-eyed, and troubled, along Anson Road. I heard Sean shouting after me:

'Remember, Sue, I love you. I'll love you always. Take care, please. I'll catch up with you again soon, so I will.'

Yes, I thought. 'Maybe you will, and maybe you won't.'

Having second thoughts, I turned around, and headed to Birchfields park across the road, and sat down on a bench, holding my head in my hands; I cried, in frustration, and renewed despair.

It was too early to call upon Sister Augustine. Looking around me it seemed as if Sean had disappeared into thin air. He was nowhere to be seen. He obviously didn't feel able to face Sister Augustine. After all, she might call him to account: what was *he* going to do about it? Did he have regular work? Doesn't he wish to do the 'right' thing and legitimise the child in the eyes of God, and how would he provide for me and the baby?

Sean had lived his life ducking and diving away from authority, whilst here was I, feeling like putty in everyone's hands. The bottom line is, I concluded, I am female. Women have few choices in life. Men, on the other hand seem to have carte blanche in terms of *their* options. That's how it looked from where I was sitting.

One day, I vowed, I'll be dependent on *no-one*. I'll earn my own money, keep my own children, and my own house. Right now, though, my life is hanging in the balance again. I will have to go grovelling to Sister Augustine to ask her for help again in finding somewhere else to live. I've broken the sacred rules of the church and society, and I have to face the consequences, one way or another.

As for Sean's professed love for me, now I knew only too well, that words come cheap. Unless they're backed up by practical deeds, and personal acts of kindness, they count for nothing.

At nine o' clock I was sitting on the other side of Sister Augustine's desk again. I had no option but to blurt out the whole saga of events. I was anxious throughout, whilst my unborn baby began kicking for Manchester United in my enormous belly, as if to beat me up for this latest, dastardly misdemeanour.

'I can't go back, Sister. All I did was to let him in. He was so unwell, and I took pity on him. What else could I do? Those Sisters would never understand, I'm sure of it.'

The elderly nun reflected silently upon the situation for a moment, endeavouring to formulate a decision. Meanwhile I heaved a huge, despairing sigh and shrank back in my chair, awaiting my fate.

'Well, now.' There was another pause before Sister Augustine said: 'Take a seat outside, why don't you; I need to make a phone call and I'll be out again directly.'

'Yes, Sister.' Slowly, I rose to my feet, dragging my suitcase containing my few possessions. Head bowed, I went to do as I was told, to sit outside her office. The scene was redolent of that of a wayward girl, awaiting her punishment from the headmistress' study, only it felt ten times worse. I knew that I *wasn't a* difficult person, and neither was I unreasonable. This was the result of a set of circumstances which conspired, unjustly, to stigmatise me, to constrain my very being and to penalise me for having 'broken' socially constructed, ideological conventions. More than anything I felt frustrated by my disempowerment.

Nervously, I found myself counting first the black diamond-shaped floor tiles of the expansive hallway, and I was halfway through counting the white intersecting tiles when the door opened and Sister Augustine, with keys a-jangling said:

I'm going to take you on somewhere else, Susan, but you must promise me that you're not going to run away again, from *this* place.'

CHAPTER 8

I was in awe of this elderly nun who was sitting beside me as she negotiated the busy streets of Manchester. It was evident that she knew, very well, her way around the whole area of the city, and far beyond. Born and bred in Ireland, her lifelong vocation in Manchester had been the mainstay of her existence.

Dressed from head to toe in black, other than that of a narrow glimpse of the white cap under her veil which enveloped her hair, she drove the vehicle with confidence, and chatted throughout the journey. Her work and devotion to God and to the community had provided her with a meaningful life, and I couldn't help comparing her with other, more ordinary women I had known, and *their* lives.

It was an irony, I thought, that here was a woman who, according to most people's views, had lived a more secluded life than most, far removed from what 'normal' womanhood was deemed to comprise: marriage, wifedom, sex and motherhood, and yet somehow she seemed to be strangely liberated. Her career involved making significant decisions about people's lives; she also drove a car at a time when most of the working classes did not own a car. Furthermore, it would be many more years before the majority of women drove vehicles in the United Kingdom, followed still by decades when they were dubbed as 'women drivers', the butt of jokes, and blame, by men who seemed to take offence at the idea of women having as much right, and as much competence behind the wheel, as they had. In addition, Sister Augustine seemed to have contact with a wide range of people and organisations around the greater Manchester area. Women in positions of authority, whose career dominated their lives, were few and far between in the nineteen-sixties.

I couldn't help comparing her life and accomplishments with that also of my mother whose existence, though she was younger, had been wholly constrained by her marriage.

Sister Augustine drove us from Victoria Park in south Manchester to Prestwich, several miles north of the city.

I remembered the only other time I'd been to Prestwich: my friend, Jenny, had invited a few girlfriends around to her house. We were all sixteen, and it was a get-together one Sunday afternoon in which we could play our favourite records at her house, and she provided us with nibbles to eat, and cider to drink. Jenny's parents were quite liberal-minded in their approval for us to drink cider moderately. All of us seemed to be quite taken with the singer, Roy Orbison, and we became slightly tipsy listening to his singles, and singing along to 'Only the lonely', 'In Dreams', and 'Crying'.

We reached the town, and Sister Augustine drove us into a residential area. Neither of us spoke of where we were heading. I had no idea where we were going. I was too polite to ask, and too grateful for being helped, whilst she clearly did not wish to discuss our actual destination.

We turned into the soon, never-to-be-forgotten road, that of Broome Lane. For years to come, I would read and hear about girls and young women who had been to 'Broome Lane', and never that of Saint Teresa's, as the convent was rightly named. Broome Lane was all that needed to be said.

She pulled up outside the convent. By this time I was beginning to feel a sense of familiarity with religious institutions. This one appeared to be a sprawling combination of historic, religious buildings, with newer, modern extensions.

I didn't learn, until several decades later, that Saint Teresa's was run by an order of nuns who became known for all the wrong reasons.

Unlike Saint Joseph's Convent, and St Joseph's Roman Catholic High School for Girls in Victoria Park where I'd slavishly worked hard in the kitchens, St Teresa's didn't instantly feel to be as friendly, from the moment I set foot inside.

'I'll leave you here now, Susan,' Sister Augustine said. 'The Sisters will take good care of you, and your baby. Goodbye, now. And good luck.'

She departed, and left me in the company of another nun, whose name was not given, but the latter told me to follow her. We entered a series of rooms and then, significantly, up a narrow winding staircase which formed the tower of the old part of the convent. It reminded me of a day visit from school to York Minster in which we had climbed the tower. It felt eery. Being so heavily pregnant, it was hard to keep up with the nun whilst carrying my case and needing to tread carefully up the awkward, narrowing steps, with nothing to hold on to but the stone wall itself.

After passing a first floor door leading off from the tower, we climbed higher and finally reached the very top. The nun opened the door to reveal a rotunda. There were three single beds and two sets of drawers. I was told that the farthest bed from the door would be mine. The nun's face was expressionless, and lacking in any warmth. She instructed me to unpack my clothes and then to return downstairs again, whereupon she would find me a job to do, since, as she put it:

'Idle hands are the devil's workshop.'

Well that's a nice welcome, I thought. What's that supposed to mean, as if I couldn't guess. Too late for me, the devil has already been and gone.

She left, and closed the door. I sat on the edge of the bed, looking around at the circular, claustrophobic room in which I was to sleep alongside two strangers.

'My God,' I said out loud. 'What sort of a place is this?' There were no windows in what passed for a bedroom. It seemed airless and cold. There was just one exit, and that led to the steep stairs I had just climbed. This had to count as another of the strangest places in which I had stayed.

Saint Teresa's was, of course, a Mother and Baby Home for unmarried girls and young women. One of those places where young women were sent, far away from home to have their baby, then leave without it.

The staircase, which I felt sure would have been responsible for many past sprained ankles, or perhaps worse, was lit by the type of lighting system where there are energy-saving buttons to press which illuminate the immediate area for a matter of minutes, before automatically switching themselves off. I couldn't imagine what sort of fire service had passed this building's inspection for so vulnerable a group of people. I immediately hastened my footsteps downwards towards the next button, positioned half way between the bottom floor and the very top. It was to become a feat of agility and mindful concentration, to move up and down the dark tower stairwell to safety, holding on to various parts of the stone wall en route.

I reached the bottom of the tower, relieved to hear voices and see daylight again.

Looking around for the same nun I wanted to regale her with the good news that the devil hadn't yet revisited me, as the steps up to the top of the tower would almost certainly deter him unless he was on a death wish.

A number of the girls, all heavily pregnant, passed me, looking as if they were on their way somewhere; some smiled, a few said hello, and I wandered into a large, untidy living room. One of the girls, a fair haired girl of about seventeen said:

'Hia, I'm Mary Ann. You must be new? Do you want to do a bit of ironing?'

Feeling bewildered, and anxious, I managed to nod, as she took me to the ironing board which stood in the middle of the room. Alongside it was a large wicker basket overflowing with baby clothes, aprons and items of clothing.

I thanked her, although I wasn't sure why and, still feeling disorientated, I slowly reached down to switch on the iron at the wall. As if in 'slow motion' I took out a piece of laundered baby clothing to smooth out the creases.

All of the day's tensions seemed to culminate in this moment, where a sense of abandonment and despair culminated in silent teardrops. I blinked them back, pretending to look out through the window, and back again through blurred vision to the tiny item of clothing that needed my attention. I felt a desolation that stands out, painfully, in my memory to this day. Swallowing hard, and trying to feign a sense of self-possession, I looked around at some of the other girls who appeared, surprisingly, to have come to terms with their institutionalisation. Perhaps, I reflected, this constituted, for them, some sort of penance that five hail Mary's didn't quite suffice; that being in this place could somehow cleanse them of their past, wicked misdemeanours.

What had I done so terribly wrong, I thought, that justified being put in here? This constituted a desperately low point for me.

For the next hour I ironed through what became my initial, introduction to the Prestwich home for unmarried mothers. Other young mums-to-be appeared, periodically, to tip more clean laundry into the wicker basket until I hoped that I had done enough for the time being. Why deny anyone else the joys of ironing fiddly baby clothes, and, besides, I certainly didn't want to be branded as an ironing queen, or the mug to be given this job every time there wasn't anyone else around who wanted to do it. I wasn't quite sure why some of these tiny clothes needed to be ironed anyway; a babygrow surely stretches across an infant, and whatever creases are left would very likely be covered in vomit within a short time of being worn? Either that, or it would soon be soiled from a terry towelling nappy, and need to be changed again anyway? I knew that I was sure to discover these things very soon for myself.

One of the pregnant girls pushed a tea trolley into the main, rectangular-shaped living room where I had been ironing; there were windows on two sides and seats placed all around the edges.

'Tea up!' she shouted.

I hoped not to appear to be too forward in helping myself to a cup of tea and several rich tea fingers. I had missed both my breakfast and mid-day meal and I was feeling distinctly empty in the pit of my stomach. Several of the girls drifted into the room and sat alongside me with their refreshments also.

I was surprised to find that many of them seemed just like me. They were friendly, educated, and interested in getting to know me, which I found heartening. I was just as intrigued to learn all about them too, and their lives.

One of the nuns scuttled into the room to make sure that we weren't becoming too comfortable, but the girls continued to chat for a while, enjoying a respite in between their allocated chores.

I learned that St Teresa's operated on the basis of the resident girls' and young women's labour: in the laundry, the kitchens, and in performing the household and cleaning chores which served the whole of the convent and the annexe for newborn babies. I was also told that, where a mother-to-be slept *before* her delivery changed after she had given birth, when each new mother was allocated a bedroom of her own in the annexe, on the floor above the nursery where her new baby would lie in one of the cots. The baby would reside in the home for six weeks, after which it was expected that it would be adopted, and the mother would leave and make her post-partum way back into the world.

The Home received basic social security benefits for each female who resided there, of which a small amount of 'spending money' was given to each girl. The rest of it went towards our 'keep' and towards the Home's running costs.

I explained to one of the girls, called Beattie, that I was going to keep my baby.

'Well, you haven't met Sister Philomena yet! She'll try to break your will. She usually succeeds. I'm just warning you, she'll give you a hard time. Her sole purpose here is to get you to sign the form to relinquish all rights to your baby. We all realise that it's probably for the best, anyway, because how else would we manage? Let's face it, we've all been put in here to take us out of mainstream society, to get rid of *the problem*.'

With that, Beattie and the other girls quickly disappeared back to their respective areas of work in the Home.

I sat for a few minutes, trying to digest what she had told me. Sister Philomena can try with all her might, but there'll be no breaking me! This is my flesh and blood; *my own child* inside me, and I will walk out of here holding my baby in my arms, with or without their blessing, I resolved. There could be no way that, after all these months of struggle, anyone was going to take away this child, but *me*. I would fight them, if need be. I would abscond with her or him, if necessary, before the six weeks is up. At least I am forearmed with knowledge that will help me, I thought.

A nun whom I hadn't yet met approached me.

'Susan? Is it Susan Linnell?'

'Yes, Sister.' I stood up and paid attention.

'I've put you on our cleaning rota, Susan,' she said, holding a clip board in her hands, 'and there's no time like the present.'

She looked around the room to make an assessment of what needed to be done.

'Could you wipe and clean all the chairs in the living room, please, with the cleaning materials you'll find in here?' She took me over to a tall cupboard in which were stored all sorts of cleaning supplies, two brooms and a vacuum cleaner.

'And when you have finished that would you also give the wooden floor surrounding the carpet square a gentle wipe clean; and lastly vacuum the rug in here. That should be enough for today, but tomorrow after breakfast I would like you to clean all our wooden staircases. They're often overlooked by the girls and we want them to look nice and clean. Now, is everything clear?'

'Yes, Sister. Thank you.'

She disappeared in haste, as if she had much to attend to.

I wondered what she would have said if I had objected to doing the work. If I had said that I am extremely tired, and have a terrible headache. That I am too advanced in my pregnancy to be undertaking hard, physical work that involves carrying a heavy vacuum cleaner, bending up and down, and dragging it across floors? Did they realise that the strain on my back from my advanced stage of pregnancy doesn't need the additional toll of physically demanding work?

But I was like all the other girls: I was a *good girl*. Only *good* girls were put in here, I decided. That's why we're in here. As the late painter, Paula Rego, asserted, *good girls* got pregnant because they did as they were told.

Wearily, I walked over to the cleaning supplies cupboard and took out some materials. I felt incredibly tired. My head was spinning with all that was happening: this new displacement into a different environment, a different regime with new rules, challenges, and people.

No one that I knew would know of my whereabouts, my new bed, the stage of my pregnancy, or know of the strain and despondency of my feelings. Nor would they care. I should be getting used to it.

After working in the living room it smelled fresh from my dusting and polishing all the plastic chairs, cleaning the wooden floor surrounds then finally vacuuming the carpet.

I had just completed the jobs when a bell sounded throughout the convent. It reminded me of the bell at school which signalled the end of one lesson and the time to make our way to the next.

A slow exodus of pregnant girls drifted towards the dining room. I followed the crowd and took my place at a counter where each of us queued up with a tray to help ourselves to the food which had been cooked by some of the girls for our supper. The meal was very basic and unappetising but, as my mother would have said:

'Beggars can't be choosers.' It seemed like I'd been relegated to the status of beggar for some time now; what else could I do, but eat it.

The remainder of the day seemed to hasten into a tired blur: the chatter of the girls, and the sight of the overseer nuns. After exchanging a few words with another girl called Lynn in the living room, I made my final ascent for the day up the steps of the bloody tower.

Breathless, trying hard to get up before the lights went out, I arrived at the bedroom to find my new room mates were already there.

'Hi, I'm Peggy,' one of the girls said, as she was putting on her dressing gown. She held out her hand to shake mine, and I felt pleased to be warmly welcomed into some sort of fold. 'Oh, gosh, you look tired.'

'I nodded. I'm Susan. Just call me Sue. I've had quite an adventure today,' I said, managing to add a light touch.

'Oh you must tell,' she implored. 'We could do with some excitement in here, couldn't we, Margaret?' She looked round at the second girl who was smiling at me whilst brushing her hair.

'Hello. Very pleased to meet you, Sue. I'm Margaret. It's nice to have a full house up here. More stories to share, more fun to be had!'

Both girls were heavily pregnant. They seemed to be very bright, personable and polite young women.

'It's nice to meet you both,' I said. 'Please excuse me if I seem to be less than sociable this evening. I am so tired. I could sleep standing up!'

'That's fine Sue, we do understand,' said Peggy. Margaret chimed in also, saying that when she first came to St Teresa's two weeks ago she almost slept solidly for the first three days, such was the anxiety she experienced. Then she said:

'Before I came here I'd never gone to bed so early in my life!'

We laughed, in unison, and I knew that they were both lovely people.

After our respective visits to the bathroom on the ground floor, we each climbed into our beds, and I was just about to turn over to go to sleep, when Margaret piped up:

'Before you go to sleep, Sue, if you need to go to wee in the night, please let me know! Just wake me up and I'll make sure those wretched lights stay on long enough for you to go down and come up again in one piece. We help each other out with this. Otherwise, we'd be stuck in the dark down there, and God knows what might happen. It can be so frightening.'

'Oh Margaret, that's very kind of you. Thank you. And the same goes for me with both of you; just wake me up and I'll do the same for you.'

We each voiced 'Night night' to the other two.

It wasn't going to be so bad, after all, I decided, with a tired sigh. Not with companions like these.

Breakfast was another basic offering. The choice between corn-flakes or toast was underwhelming. If we were lucky we might have been able to sneak a bowl of cornflakes *and* a piece of toast, but there was nothing so extravagant as marmalade or jam available to spread on the toast. This 'menu' was repeated every day, with no exceptions. Moreover, it appeared that the Sisters disapproved of coffee. They probably thought that it stimulated unwelcome sensations; another visit from the Devil. Tea was the only hot drink on offer.

I soon learned that the food, in general, was regarded as substandard by all the girls. Every single day of the week the mid-day meal comprised potatoes *boiled in their skins*; one other vegetable, usually overcooked carrots, peas or cabbage, and a small portion of meat; fish if it was Friday. The meat was frequently a thin slice of cold meat such as ham, spam or corned beef and, not once was the meal accompanied by gravy or a sauce of any kind.

Supper consisted usually of a sandwich, or occasionally soup and a roll was offered instead. The meals were, to say the least, unappetizing and poor in nutritional content. My former school Head of Domestic Science, Miss Horne, would have been outraged.

At weekends, when most of us were given respite from our chores, a group of us would stroll down Broome Lane to go to the nearby newsagent to buy snacks with our allocated spending money. Chatting, frequently laughing, we enjoyed our freedom from housework.

All heavily pregnant, we descended upon the shop, deliberating at length whether to buy a small packet of biscuits, or some potato crisps, peanuts or even a chocolate bar. Each time I glanced at the newsagent I wondered what he made of us all. He would observe our every move with eagle-eyed scrutiny.

Did he think it inevitable that, since our moral standards were so contemptible, he risked ending up with half his stock disappearing under our voluminous clothes and into our knickers, bound for the Home? We must have looked, at times, to be audacious in our giggles and high spirits which, in truth, was the result of being happy to be 'let out', and not to be undertaking domestic work in the Home, for once. Or as 'bad girls' did he imagine us to be louche? After all, weren't men deemed to have 'uncontrollable desires', and was he running away with the idea that women like us existed to fan those desires?

Both presumptions could not have been further from the truth.

Our joviality must have given the impression that we had not a care in the world, but it was a veneer.

The truth was that every single girl in that Home was suffering greatly; from being rejected by family, sometimes a lover also; by physical encumbrances and the tolls of an unwanted pregnancy; from the injustices arising from becoming a social pariah. We girls together, though, strengthened our defences, albeit fleetingly, in developing close bonds of sisterhood. Patriarchal society had 'set us up', sentenced us, criminalised and incarcerated us for 'crimes' against society and religion of which we were not guilty; at a critical time in our lives when each of us was silently crying out for genuine love and support.

During the weeks that followed I witnessed a river of tears; emotional outpourings, and instances of holding hands, and clinging on to each other that I have yet to experience in any other situation. Sorrow and pain was part of the course. Even before our deliveries we became mothers to each other, helping with the pains of labour, and dispensing solace to try to soothe wounds that could never heal.

On my second night at St Teresa's, the three of us lay in our beds in the darkness, bumps facing skywards, as Peggy, Margaret and I exchanged our individual stories.

Had we lived in the era of fly-on-the wall reality TV, I am convinced that it would have constituted a major hit series as we disclosed the experiences that had brought us here.

In the bed nearest to me Margaret began, light heartedly:

'Oh, gosh, when I think of it, I was *so* green. I had really looked forward to my friend's party. I'd bought a new outfit, a gorgeous scarlet mini dress with a sparkly hem and neckline. It was quite modest, really, though, by Carnaby Street standards. I thought I looked the bees knees. I was a virgin, saving myself for some lucky boy I dreamed about who would one day come my way, and for whom I'd make the perfect wife. Well, this party was, I suppose, my first real party; you know, with grown up people and alcohol flowing.'

Margaret was twenty years old. She was from Bolton, and had worked in a solicitor's office. She was considering applying to go to university to study Law. She had a lovely open face, and a shock of short, well cut, brunette hair.

'Anyway, there was I, making for the nibbles and doing what I thought was mingling. The friend who had invited me seemed to be taken up with her new boyfriend, and I just flowed around, as if I was enjoying myself. I was drinking Babycham and then this boy asked me if I liked Cherry B. I must have said that I'd try it, and it was, I recall, quite nice. Well the rest is history. I must have got absolutely legless on Cherry B's. I can't remember much about the rest of the evening, or the boy. All I know is that my friend pushed me into a taxi to get home, and the boy seemed to disappear into thin air!'

'So you had sex with him then?' I asked.

'I must have. Let's put it like this: I've been stone cold sober ever since, and not been as much as a whisker's distance of any boy. The next minute I was missing my period, had sore tits, and was peeing for England.'

'Oh, Margaret, how awful for you. How do you feel about this?' She seemed to be bearing this disaster with uncanny resilience.

'Well, I wish I could say that at least I'd had a great time, that the sex was an earth shattering experience, but I can't remember any of it! The next day I realised that I'd bled. It was only later on that I realised that my hymen had been broken because I was sore too. He walked away with my virginity. It wasn't the only thing I lost because I went home without my new mini half-slip that I'd bought to wear under the dress. He probably wore it over his head as he made his escape.'

Peggy and I convulsed with laughter at Margaret's description of the non-event, but we knew, in our hearts, that it was a really terrible thing that had happened to her, and that she was trying to put on a brave face about it all.

'He was a shit-head,' announced Peggy. 'Knowing it was going to be a one-night stand he should have worn a condom. Listen to *me* talking, though, because my man was no different,' she said, as she suddenly became very serious.

'I was in a relationship for ten months, and it was only when I told him that I was pregnant that he announced that he was married. I never saw him again. An utter bastard, that's what. I had no idea.'

Peggy was the oldest of the three of us at twenty two years old. She was from Knutsford in Cheshire, and her parents had asked the local priest where she could go to have her baby. The priest himself had driven her up to 'far flung' Prestwich.

None of our parents came anywhere near Saint Teresa's during the whole time we were there. It was the same for all of the girls. It wasn't the sort of place with which most people would want to be associated, or to be seen. Besides, the whole idea was to pretend that the need to be in there hadn't occurred in the first place.

A week had passed and I decided to write a brief note to my parents to let them know where I was. I wrote to my older sister, Jean, to tell her the same. Neither party acknowledged my letter.

I also decided to write to Sean. Since it was his baby I was expecting, I felt that he should know where I was living now. He responded straight away, writing from Notting Hill Gate in London, and sending me his love. We exchanged letters, and in particular he wrote that he had been thinking about the name of the baby, and that he hoped that if it was a boy we could call him Jimmy or, if a girl, then Kitty, after two of his siblings who lived back home in Kilkenny.

After writing to my friend Jenny to let her know all that had happened to me I received a lovely reply from her, by return post, saying that she had been concerned about me, not having heard anything from me for a while, and that she and her mother would like to visit me. On reading her letter I was actually quite tearful; so happy that someone cared enough about me to want to see me.

On the following Sunday one of the nuns, sister Agnes, came looking for me to tell me that a friend of mine and her mother were waiting to see me in one of the small meeting rooms. She led the way to a room which, I was to learn later, was normally used for adopting parents who came to take away one of the babies.

When I walked into the room Jenny immediately rushed up to me and flung her arms around me, and her mother came over to hug me at the same time. It was a difficult moment. They held on to me tightly. I struggled hard not to cry. That anyone actually seemed to care touched me deeply. We sat down together, huddled in a corner, and I tried to keep the conversation light-hearted. I told them about the awful food; the boiled potatoes in their skins, whose daily odour filled the whole place; the bedroom up the tower, likening it to an abode akin to that of Mary Queen of Scots', only smaller and without the windows; and about the lovely girls with whom I shared my 'tower bedroom'.

'You both look so smart,' I said, and I meant it. Jenny was wearing a lovely, colourful mini dress with matching bag, and her mum was wearing a pale blue, two-piece suit. I was reminded of how people tried to look nice when they go out visiting. I felt it more acutely because I was dressed in a loose, unfashionable dress which I considered distinctly dowdy and unattractive. Life in the Home didn't entail 'dressing' for any occasion. There was never anything to dress up for except, perhaps, on one of my antenatal visits to St Mary's hospital in Manchester, in which I tried to pretend that I was like any other, normal mother-to-be, and not coming from a Home for unmarried mothers.

Jenny's mother handed me a beautiful bunch of chrysanthemums, while Jenny gave me a carefully wrapped present, bound with yellow ribbon. I felt overwhelmed.

'Please open it now,' begged Jenny.

I carefully untied the ribbon. I wanted to save it as a keepsake of their visit. Inside, enclosed in tissue paper, was a beautiful lemon-coloured baby blanket, with tiny embroidered flowers embellished across it. I thought it to be the most exquisite little blanket I had ever seen.

Their kindness and generosity lifted my spirits for long after-wards. Jenny's mum promised to visit again soon. I apologised for not being able to offer them a drink, and also for not being allowed to take them into other parts of the Home. It was by no mean co-incidence that what few callers there were to this 'house of fallen women' were kept quite separate from the spectacle of other heavily pregnant girls, the nuns, the cries of babies, and day-to-day goings on.

When they had gone home I put the flowers in a large metal container that I found in the kitchen and placed them in the living room for everyone to enjoy. Besides, there was no natural light in our bedroom. Meanwhile, I cherished my first, and only, baby gift, the gorgeous little yellow blanket that would soon swaddle my precious baby.

By this time I had already been summoned to attend a meeting with the dreaded Sister Philomena. She was a nun in her later years, straight-laced and 'on a mission', just as Beattie had warned me.

The tiny nun, bent forward with osteoarthritis, was seated on the other side of an enormous wooden desk.

'Sit down, Susan,' she said, opening a file in which I presumed my details were held. 'I see that your baby is due in around four weeks' time.'

'Yes, Sister.'

'As you know we are responsible for finding good, loving Catholic parents for all the babies born to the girls here at Saint Teresa's. Rest assured, we will find a lovely couple who will wish to adopt your baby, Susan. And we will………….'

Without hesitation, I had to quickly summon the courage to intervene, to stop the getaway car from running too far in the wrong direction.

'I'm sorry to interrupt, Sister Philomena, but my situation is different.' I took a deep breath, then: 'I want to keep my baby.'

There was an abrupt pause, followed by a glower of immense disapproval, laser-piercing in its projection towards me from under her crotchety brow.

'Susan.' She shook her head. 'You shock me. I am convinced that you will think more carefully about such an unwise decision. It would be extremely selfish of you, given that there are so many poor couples who cannot conceive of a child. They are longing to provide a decent Catholic home to a baby, whilst it is clear to me that you will *not* be in a position to do so. Please reconsider this folly and come and see me again next week at the same time.'

'With respect, Sister Philomena, I have given this matter eight months of consideration and I wish to keep my baby. I will, though, come and see you again next week.'

I rose clumsily, and left the room, letting out a huge breath of relief at having managed to impart the unwelcome news. I felt like a nervous wreck in having cleared the first fence in what felt like the start of a Grand National event at Aintree.

If it hadn't been for the camaraderie of the girls in the evenings as we watched television, or the strolls down Broome Lane going to the newsagents, and the precious night-time chats with Peggy and Margaret, I don't think that I could have coped in such an unforgiving place like St Teresa's. We were all treated disdainfully by most of the nuns, as girls who had transgressed and were in need of redemption.

And yet, the girls' babies provided the lifeblood of the nuns' service, literally; a religious order dedicated to helping childless couples by providing infants from those they clearly regarded as 'unfit mothers', in exchange for substantial donations, thus also 'saving' babies from a life of unmitigated degradation.

One day, after carrying a bucket up the stairs of the tower, and scrubbing and wiping dry each stone step, I must have been just over half the way down, on my hands and knees, when a door burst open from the first floor and Mother Superior came hurrying downwards, carrying some documents. She reached as far as my bucket, which I swiftly moved aside so that she could pass, however, as she looked down at me she instructed:

'Kiss the hem of Mother Superior's robe.'

Still on my knees, and crammed against the wall of the cold tower, I slowly reached for the garment as she stood to watch. I pulled the hem towards my lips, then let it go, clumsily fumbling to pull back my heavy frame to let her pass. Numb with shock, and feeling worthless, I resumed my task slowly, as she disappeared to the ground floor. I couldn't believe what had just happened. But it had. It was a belittling experience I would share with Peggy and Margaret that evening as we lay in our beds.

Peggy spewed: 'I think I might have been tempted to chuck the bucket over her feet. They think they're in the bloody middle ages, these sodding nuns. What a bitch! I can't wait to get out of this bloody place.'

Peggy was the most angry of the three of us. She felt bitterly betrayed by her ex-lover, her parents and by society, and she espoused the feelings of all of us about the way in which we were so horribly treated.

After supper each evening, those of us who had not yet had our babies sometimes watched television and joked and chatted away the evening, or until 'lights out'.

Amongst us was a young woman with Downs' Syndrome who was also heavily pregnant, and she wanted to join in the fun and banter.

The other girls were all kind to her.

'Hey, Eloise,' one girl shouted across to her, 'what are you going to call *your* baby?'

Eloise thought carefully for a moment and then answered:

'I'm not sure, really. Maybe if it's a boy I'll call him my dad's name, Fred. But if it's a girl I might call her my mum's name, Irene.' She beamed a beautiful wide smile.

Eloise had gorgeous red, curly hair, and we could only pity this poor young woman who would have to go through the pains of labour like the rest of us, not really understanding why.

In the nineteen sixties people with learning difficulties were either kept in the family home until their parents died, or frequently put into a Home where their freedoms were severely restricted. Some of us shared privately between ourselves that Eloise must have been subjected to dreadful experiences of exploitation.

Later, that evening, Sister Agnes came into the living room and made a beeline for me.

'Susan, there's a telephone call for you. It's your father.'

I was shocked. Why would Dad telephone me? He hadn't been in touch at all, so it had to be important. I followed the nun to an office where a telephone receiver lay on the desk. Sister Agnes turned to leave, and she closed the door behind her.

'Hello Dad, it's Susan.' I heard additional coins dropping into a public telephone box.

'Hello Susan.' There was a pause. Then muffles. He didn't sound right.

'What's up Dad?'

'I'm phoning to tell you……' His voiced cracked. He cleared his throat and resumed: 'Your Nan died today.'

I sat back. My beloved grandmother, the person to whom I had been very close, throughout my childhood, and with whom I had gone to stay for weeks at a time in my school holidays, was now gone forever.

'Oh, no, Dad. I'm shocked…….. Oh, no,……… I'm so sorry, Dad. Was she ill? How did that happen?'

'We've been staying with her. Your mum's been nursing her. She got weaker and weaker and became poorly. She just gave up, and…….' His voice broke into a flood of sobs. *It was the only time I had ever heard my father cry.* His adored mother had passed away.

Mum took hold of the receiver and curtailed the phone call.

'Your Dad's upset. We'll be in touch, Susan. Alright love. Bye for now.' And that was it.

I felt upset too. And I felt really sorry for Dad. My dear Nan had left us.

I wandered back into the main part of the convent, and made my way slowly up the steep steps of the tower. Lying on my bed, I shed a few tears as I recalled all the fabulous times my sparky Nan had made me laugh; there were so many wonderful memories of her I held dear. I suddenly remembered, however, her most recent letter in which, as usual, she had been very outspoken and blunt, having been told of my pregnancy. She had written to urge me to get married, for the sake of the baby. She said that if I didn't marry and legitimise the relationship then the baby would be 'a bastard', and I would have to live with the consequences of that.

I was shocked and hurt. The only way that I could recon-cile her abrasive words was to think that she was a woman of her time. She was born in Victorian times, into a world where labels and behaviours were even more stigmatizing than those which I was currently experiencing. It was easy to forgive Nan. I knew that she had loved me, and that she thought that she was giving me the best advice possible. I believed it to be misguided, though, and I wanted to remember her always as the strong-minded grandmother and the source of inspiration that she had always been to me.

I didn't hear another word from Mum or Dad whilst I was in the Home. I wasn't invited to the funeral and, other than by writing a letter to them, I had no direct means of reaching them. Even then, I deduced, they may not have been at home. They were obviously making arrangements and sorting out Nan's effects in her council house in order to hand back the house to the local authority. I knew that they were busy but, above all things, I felt very sad that I didn't have an opportunity to pay my last respects to such a dearly loved, close relative who had exerted an enormous influence upon my life. The decision was out of my hands. I was, after all, pregnant and 'disgraced', residing in a Home for unmarried mothers. It had been decided that I was better kept out of the frame, no doubt under the pretence that things might be difficult enough for me to cope with.

On a Wednesday morning, two weeks before my baby was due, I prepared to attend one of my last antenatal appointments at St Mary's Hospital on Oxford Road in Manchester. I set off early, catching a bus in what was the early-morning rush hour from Prestwich into Manchester.

The bus was packed with people travelling to work. I had not managed to find a vacant seat, and I was one of a number of people standing in the aisle of the ground floor of the bus, holding on to a looped leather strap which suspended from the ceiling.

Fortunately, a kind young man stood up from one of the side seats and offered me his seat.

I was really grateful, because managing such a balancing act, especially when the bus turned corners had become difficult, and I thanked him, as he took my place in the aisle.

It was when I felt relaxed, and comfortable in my seat between two other commuters that I became aware of a slight, uneasy twinge in my lower abdomen. As we neared Manchester, these bouts of discomfort became more noticeable, and I began to wonder if they signified the start of labour pains.

In St Mary's hospital a young gynaecologist examined me and he seemed positively elated as he diagnosed that my baby was well and truly on its way! I had the distinct impression that I was his first patient whose cervix, he observed, had softened, and its dilations diagnosed. He seemed excited at his observations.

'Yes, Miss Linnell, I think you are experiencing the start of your contractions!' He spoke with a huge grin. 'It would appear that the baby is a little early, but very often first births are.'

'Oh, goodness! But I haven't brought a wash bag or my night-clothes!' I said, taken aback by the news.

'Don't worry. That's quite alright,' he said, 'you have plenty of time yet to go back home and collect your things, then come back here to be admitted this afternoon.'

When I arrived back at Saint Teresa's the first thing I wanted to do was to look for Peggy and Margaret to tell them of my news.

There were lots of hugs and tears, and good wishes, and finally I blew hasty goodbye kisses to my favourite pregnant girlfriends. I was just about to leave Saint Teresa's for a second time that day when one of the girls called over to me to say that Sister Agnes had just received a telephone call in the office from someone who had asked to speak to me. What timing! I had only received one other telephone call since I came into the Home, and now this was a truly inconvenient moment as I was anxious to catch another bus straight back into town again, to return to the hospital as quickly as possible.

The familiar voice on the line stopped me in my tracks. I sat down, clutching my packed case, surprised at his timing. How strange this was. It was none other than Sean, and it was the first time that he had telephoned the Home.

'I miss you, Sue; darling Sue. I want to hold you and love you and take care of you. How are you, and my baby?' I hoped the nun hadn't gleaned what Sean had said. She would never have understood and approved; not for a moment. After all, she might have been forgiven for thinking that if he loved me that much, then what was I doing in here?

Sister Agnes continued to rifle through a free standing, metal filing cabinet and showed no signs of leaving me to hold a private conversation. I felt uncomfortable and restricted in what I could say.

'Sean, I started in labour this morning. I'm about to leave, to catch a bus to take me into town again, to St Mary's hospital, to have the baby.'

'Oh, my God!' he exclaimed. 'Jesus Christ! I'm coming up! I'll see you soon,' he cried in shock. The phone went down, and I reached over the desk to put the receiver back in place.

CHAPTER 9

I felt a mixture of great anticipation, tinged with a little nervousness. A *mammoth* event lay immediately ahead of me. I couldn't wait for my baby to arrive! I set off down Broome Lane towards the bus stop for central Manchester.

Suddenly I was seized with a burning need to tell Mum what was happening; to defy my father's warning not to phone her. I knew that Dad would be in work, and my younger sister Kay would be at school.

'Mum, I just wanted to tell you that I've started in labour, and I'm on my way back to St Mary's.'

'Alright love.' She paused. 'I'm going to close the shop. I'll meet you in Stephenson's Square. Okay?'

I felt so happy that she wanted to see me, if only for a little while.

Mum stepped off the bus, and put her arm around my shoulder, as we walked onwards in the direction of Piccadilly.

'Now don't worry, Susan. Everything's going to be alright.'

'Thanks for coming, Mum. I do appreciate it.'

I hadn't seen my mother for some while. Dad had made sure of that. But in this instance he had not been around to stop her.

As we neared Oxford Road we stopped at a Chemist's shop.

'Do you have some soap and a flannel; toothpaste, and so on?' Mum asked.

I thought for a moment.

'I must admit that I only have a tiny piece of soap, and my old flannel has two big holes in it. I'm okay for toothpaste though.'

'Take this,' she said, handing me a pound note, 'get what you need.'

We stood in the shop as I quickly picked out a nice pink flannel and a bar of Imperial Leather soap, which I thought had a lovely fragrance, and seemed a treat for this special occasion.

The hospital was very busy. My contractions were uncomfortable by this time and a porter was advised to take me in a wheelchair up to a ward, where Mum stayed with me, and kept me company while I waited to be admitted. After about a half an hour she turned to me apologetically:

'Susan, I'm sorry, love, but I have to go home. Your Dad will want his tea, and Kay will be home from school shortly.'

'It's alright, Mum, I know you have to go. Thanks for coming with me. It's so nice to see you again.'

'Now, remember, everything will be okay, I'm sure.'

She turned to go, and I saw a glimpse of conflicting emotions in her face. I knew that she felt torn, and I did wonder whether she would dare to tell my father about our meeting, or whether it was a matter best left unsaid.

From everything I had read about childbirth I knew that breathing calmly, and trying to relax was going to help, and so I tried my best to distract my thoughts from the pain. I had missed having a mid day meal and therefore I was so pleased when, at five o' clock, I was offered some food and finally taken to the bed that was going to be mine for the duration of my stay.

No sooner had I eaten, but I was whisked off to a room where a nurse wielded an oversized electric shaver, plugged into the mains electricity, and applied it with gusto to my pubic hair. How deftly the nurse wafted the razor around my nether regions in what was regarded then as a necessary pre-natal procedure.

Back on the ward, the curtains were drawn around my bed and I was given my first, and only ever, enema. Within minutes, surprised by the expedience of its effects, I clambered out of bed quickly and rushed to the nearby toilets. It was an experience never to be forgotten. Sloping back towards my bed on the ward, with seemingly the entire length of my bowel cleared of all its contents I felt slightly unsteady, having needed to get washed and dried amidst my contractions, as the intensity and frequency of them gathered pace. A nurse came to check me periodically, and then left me alone again.

I was getting used to facing difficult moments on my own.

At eight o' clock I was taken to a delivery room, and transferred to a labour table. A midwife called Claire introduced herself to me. All the staff were female, and they must have known that I was a single woman. They treated me with the utmost kindness and care, and I felt in good hands. Claire advised me to listen carefully to her, throughout, saying that she would guide me through the birth, every step of the way. What an experience, I reflected. This must surely be one of *the* momentous times of my life. I was excited, and nervous at the same time.

As the contractions became more painful I was given a mouth-piece, attached to a supply of gas and air, and the midwife told me to use it to inhale from when a contraction was about to start.

'Right,' said Claire, 'I'm going to break your waters.' She reached within me and pinched the sac of amniotic fluid that had been my baby's home for almost nine months.

Suddenly, the double doors of the room burst open and, to my enormous surprise, a Nursing Sister brought in Sean.

'Susan, the father of your baby wishes to see you. He can stay for a little while, and then he must leave.'

I was shocked by his arrival. Sean rushed towards me and flung his arms around me as I lay on the table. All of the staff left us alone for a brief interlude.

'Oh my God, Sue. I came straight up. I love you, and I can't wait to see little Jimmy or Kitty.' He kissed my damp brow. After an inhalation of gas and air, feeling half stupefied, I asked him, nonsensically, for a glass of orange juice.

'Oh, Sue,' he said anxiously, I don't know where to get any, but is there anything else I can do to help?'

'Water. Water please. Need to drink. Can you cool my face?' I said, breathlessly, feeling the effects of the pain.

Sean hurtled around the theatre, looking for a glass. Panicking, he found a tumbler and rushed over to a tap to pour some water for me.

Another contraction started and I put the gas and air to my face, grimacing with the pain. When the contraction subsided he lifted my head upwards and put the glass to my lips for me to sip. Sean then raced around the room to look for something to wipe my face. Grasping at some paper towels on the wall he wet them under the tap and quickly dashed over and dabbed them all over my sweating face.

Sean was excitedly uttering all manner of things which, by this point, I could not assimilate. All that I could do was concentrate on the biggest job of my life.

The midwife, followed by three nurses came back into the theatre and he was told that it was time for him to leave. He kissed me on my cheek, beaming with happiness, and I managed to raise half a smile back.

'You're doing just great!' he shouted, as he was ushered out of the room.

'I love you, Sue,' he yelled again from the corridor, and the door swung shut.

We were left to get on with the serious business.

Midway between contractions Claire said,

'I'm going to cut you, now,' deliberately giving me no notice; no chance to squirm or fret. The sharp incision into my flesh seared through me and I cried out. Then the more urgent pains of labour ravaged my body and consumed my attention.

'Push hard, Susan. *Now!* Give it all your might! *A big push!*' Claire urged.

I pushed my hardest. 'Very good. Your baby's head is there, and now, another big push for me Susan, please!'

With every last bit of energy I could muster, I gave an almighty, hard, protracted push, grunting deeply from a place I had no idea was within me, and suddenly the rest of the baby scudded away from me. Soaked in sweat, I lay exhausted and completely drained.

'Oh gosh,' I said, sobbing, as I listened to the cries of new life. It was ten-thirty precisely, on Wednesday evening, eighteenth of September, nineteen sixty-eight.

'You have a beautiful little boy,' the midwife said.

The top end of my bed was lifted so that I could sit up and see him.

'Is he alright?' I wept, as some nurses began to clean up the pool of blood and clots that surrounded my back and legs.

'Now you can see for yourself, she said, placing a tiny bundle with a little red face into my arms.

'What are you going to call him?' said a kind nurse.

'Jimmy. Oh, he's so beautiful,' I cried. 'I can't believe it. My beautiful little Jimmy.'

The doors to the delivery room flung open again and Sean rushed towards me, in a state of great jubilation.

'You are amazing!' he cried. "Look what you've done. You're so fantastic!' He gazed down at his son, and wept. We both did.

After a few minutes my precious baby was lifted from my arms, Sean was ushered out for a second time, and I was lowered down flat on my back again. Shortly afterwards, a young male doctor came into the theatre and parked himself between my legs.

'I'm here to stitch you,' he said, lifting both of my ankles in turn and placing each foot aloft into a stirrup, legs akimbo. Before giving birth I would have squirmed with embarrassment at such indignity. Now, sheer physical exhaustion and relief at having successfully come through the other side reduced me to a happy state of nonchalant indifference.

He proceeded to thread a needle with suture and then, painstakingly, stitch up the incision which had been made to enlarge the birth canal. Here was a stitchsmith like no other. To me, this seemed to be an odd affair. For him, it was business as usual. He appeared, for all the world, as if his day job was normal.

Washed and stitched up, I was wheeled back to the ward where my baby lay waiting for me.

Sean appeared again, this time on the ward, and came to behold his new born. He was overcome with emotion, and admiration for what I had apparently pulled off. He told me how clever I was, pledging to love me forever, and little Jimmy too. I was tired, and unused to such heaped praise. I hadn't achieved it alone. I'd had the help of a fantastic team of women. Women helping women. That's how life is.

That evening as I rested back into my pillows, baby fed and sound asleep, I marvelled at the wonder of new life, at this tiny miracle who had survived all the odds during the difficult period of his gestation. My love for him had been sealed long before I first set eyes on him. But now he was real, he was in the world with me, and bound to me by love at its purest.

Mid twentieth-century maternity care involved lengthier stays in hospital for new mothers and babies than is the case today. Guidance on the care of the infant, dealing with feeding problems, offering physiotherapy and exercise for new mothers, in addition to enabling them to have sufficient rest, was an integral part of post-natal care in hospital.

I recalled an instance, as a young teenager, of my mother telling me that it was customary for new mothers to be called to go to the chapel during their hospital stay to be 'churched.' I asked her what that meant and she replied that it was a ritual of cleansing, the church's way of purifying the mother after giving birth, in addition to giving thanks for the child. I remember questioning this practice. If childbirth was a natural phenomenon, then why were women regarded as needing to be cleansed?

Now *my* turn came. I was given an appointment and asked to attend the hospital chapel on one particular morning. I wasn't sufficiently confident to question this age-old tradition. I sat there dutifully, whilst the robed cleric, wearing full regalia, presided over my head, asking God to purify me after the rigours of childbirth. I resented every second of it. Who was he, or any other male to presume that I was in any way unclean?

Some years later I came to learn how mankind has dictated that women, not only after giving birth, but during times of menstruation, are viewed as unclean and needing to be ostracised from others in some societies and not allowed to prepare food, to cook or serve others. I railed at the fact that although males have their own sets of bodily fluids this has never, in any way been regarded as impure, and neither are they required to be cleansed after ejaculation. But, I supposed, they never anticipated themselves to be the providers of meals.

My stay in St Mary's Maternity Hospital lasted for ten days, during which time my friend, Jenny, and her mum came to visit me again, and this time they were eager to see the baby. Surprisingly also, my parents came to visit me one Sunday afternoon. It was the first time Dad had seen me since he put me into that terrible night hostel for destitute women.

Theirs was a short visit during which, for once, my father had very little to say. A fair assumption would be that he was still mourning the loss of his mother, however I also sensed that he felt uncomfortable in this female-centric environment. He could exist perfectly happily as the only male within the family simply because he dominated it, and because it was in the private, domestic sphere behind closed doors; here though, in a hospital which was run mainly by women, for women, he appeared distinctly ill at ease; out of his depth.

It became obvious however that there was another, underlying reason for their visit.

Dad had previously made quite clear his views regarding what he believed I should do to resolve my current set of 'problems'. Now, glancing down at his grandson, and never having had the opportunity to have the son he had always wanted, it was crystal clear that I was not going to give up this precious child to be handed over to anyone else. Unusually, this time, he relied upon my mother to do the talking for him, in alluding to, and emphasising, his second proposal.

First, Mum commented favourably on the weight and size of their grandchild. Then she told me that my sister Jean had informed her that the terraced house next door to where she and her family lived in Openshaw, just outside Manchester, had become vacant. Furthermore, she said that Jean would be prepared to speak to the landlord on our behalf, if we had plans to marry. Gone were the hitherto subtle hints and advice that marriage was the panacea for my 'ills'; replaced now with clearly defined plans which would resolve the next predicament which I was about to have to face: that of how, and where to move on to, from Saint Teresa's. The pressure bearing upon me now felt onerous and all-encompassing.

I was only too aware that it would be financially impossible for me to live in such a house on my own, with just with my baby. Furthermore, choices involving anything other than *my* taking care of Jimmy simply weren't available to me. Those were for the better off who could afford childcare, or for those whose own mothers offered to look after the baby whilst the new mother went out to work. Those opportunities didn't exist for me.

In addition, my 'pie in the sky' ideas about hoping to be able to obtain work, living in a residence with my baby where I could become a housekeeper, now seemed ridiculously naive; after all, time was up. Moreover, as I gazed into Jimmy's gurgling, tiny face I realised just how dependent my little newborn was going to be on me, twenty four hours a day, for some time to come.

No, the daunting prospect now loomed heavily upon me that, only if Sean and I were to marry would I be able to move forwards; in what way I hadn't ever imagined, or wanted, but the day would soon come when I would be expected to leave St. Teresa's, and I knew that I could never risk homelessness with an infant. He would be taken from me forcibly by the authorities, and I would be back at square one, *and* without my precious son.

I was in a corner, and I knew it.

Back in St Teresa's, with a nice modern room of my own in the newer part of the convent, my baby lay fast asleep in the long nursery below, lined up with other infants. His cot lay directly under my bedroom. The annexe's paper thin walls and flooring enabled me to hear his cries. All the new mums remarked upon how Jimmy had quite a distinctive cry from all the other babies. His cry started with a high pitched squeal, and miaowed around to a low pitched howl; my darling baby. I think I would have picked out his characteristic sounds even if he had been as far away as in the old tower!

We all took it in turns to undertake night duties, and to alert other mums to their babies' need for a feed. However, when I wasn't on night duty I didn't need a call because I would wake to his cries every time, however deep my sleep. Whatever the hour, I would jump out of bed, fling my coat around my shoulders and over my nightdress, and rush downstairs immediately to pacify him, to hold him, feed him, and tell him how much I loved him. After changing his nappy I would make sure that he was sleepy again and lie him down in his snuggly blanket before going back upstairs to catch up on some sleep. It was late September and the song that was at the top of the hit parade was The Beatles' 'Hey Jude'. The nuns allowed us to listen to the radio and this song rang out in the nursery several times a day for many weeks on end. Every one of the new mums used to sing along to all seven minutes of it. Our babies were fed, changed and bathed to the sounds of 'Hey Jude'.

The annexe was a happier place to be in than the boiled-potato-in-skins-smelling, main part of the convent. The total joy of new life, of a warm Autumn, the songs, and the new freedom from the hapless chores, other than those involving one's baby, gave rise to a more relaxed atmosphere where the nuns did not choose to tread.

Their job was done. They had selected their haloed, Catholic parents-to-be, and pre-matched them with the tiny infants who filled the cots in the nursery.

When Jimmy was three weeks' old Sister Philomena tried for a final time to crack a nut that refused to break. As usual, I nervously knocked on the door, and entered, waiting to be told to sit down. She was already scowling and prepared for the response that met her salutation:

'I don't suppose, for one minute, Susan, that you've had a change of heart? You would be all the more sensible for it, and there's still time to change your mind.'

'No, Sister. I love my baby with all my heart. I will be keeping him.'

'Then you're one of the most selfish, cruel and undeserving girls I have ever had the displeasure of knowing. I pity your poor infant! You'd better get out of here,' she rasped.

I wasn't expecting such a vituperous rebuke; harsh, may be, but this was the fourth time that she had tried to pressurise me into giving up my son. I got up from my chair and managed to hold back my tears until I had closed the door. I sobbed all the way back to the nursery where my post-natal, hormonally charged head fell apart, and it was all that I could do but to weep into the little yellow blanket that swaddled my baby boy.

'No one, absolutely no-one, is ever going to take you from me,' I cried. He looked into my face, blinked, and hiccuped. I held his gorgeous, soft face to mine, and my tears touched his cheeks. I never want to see that woman again, I thought. Some Christian woman she pretends to be; fully institutionalised, and devoid of humanity, one day she was going to have to work very hard on Saint Peter before he would even *think* about budging those gates.

Almost every day, it seemed, one of the girls started in labour. Many of them were distressed and tearful. These were no ordinary labours or births. They had no mum to reassure them, no partner to share their pains; no hands, other than ours to clasp theirs. Worse to come, each girl hardly dared to love her little one too much in the six weeks they had together. But they all did. How could they *not*?

Peggy, in particular, found her delivery incredibly hard. But she, Margaret and I shrieked with laughter, when she recounted how, throughout her excruciating, long labour, when the pains were at their worst, she screamed hysterically, at full throttle:

'You Bastard! You bloody Bastard! I bloody hate you!…………….' And how her words rang out well beyond the delivery room; words aimed at her ex-lover, the very same who had walked away after telling her he was married.

All of our laughter turned to tears as we sobbed for her, and sobbed for ourselves too. Six arms entwined, holding tightly on to each other. We were like The Three Graces, but in an ungainly scrum. Weren't they all, though, bloody bastards? What did *they* care about our pain, our lived hell; our gut-wrenching, tear-filled kisses before having to walk away from our own flesh and blood for the very last time.

Margaret's departure from Saint Teresa's is etched deeply within my memory. It was killing. A taxi was waiting outside for her, to take her on a one-way journey back to Bolton. She had unintentionally crossed paths with the arrival of the couple who had come to claim her baby boy; the little darling whom, after six weeks, Margaret adored and had *so not wanted* to give up. Too late. She had signed Sister Philomena's form; her mother had implored her on the telephone to come home and to walk away from her infant. I watched Margaret's pathetic figure, weeping uncontrollably, as she climbed into the back of the taxi, and then, holding her head in her hands, as the taxi disappeared slowly down Broome Lane. I, too, cried for her, and all the others, at the cruelty of it all; for the desperate years ahead without their firstborn and, in some instances, their *only* child.

That night, I knew that I had to come to terms with a decision that had already been ordained. The deal was this: in order to keep my baby, I had no other choice but to marry Sean.

Society at this time decreed that I could not possibly care for my child *and* get housing; *or* get benefits, *or* get a job that would provide for both me and my child. Our social infrastructure was such that only with a *husband*, would I be offered a tenancy, and it was assumed that the said husband would provide for us. Despicably, such were the anomalies of those times that even having an *absent, irresponsible* or *violent* husband would still conspire to allow me to keep my child.

There was no question about what I should do. Come hell or high water I was going to keep my son.

CHAPTER 10

Six weeks later, on the morning of my wedding on the second of November, nineteen sixty-eight, I looked into the cloudy mirror in the dingy toilet of the back-to-back house in Openshaw, and spoke out loud to my reflection:

'I'll get a divorce.'

What a sham of a wedding it was. Dressed in a green two-piece suit, I walked up the aisle of The Holy Name in Rusholme, the very Roman Catholic church about which I had lied to Mother Superior in London when she had asked me where I had married. Only this time I wasn't wearing a Woolworth's ring. I could do better than that: I was wearing an inexpensive gold band that I had bought and paid for myself. Sean, as you might now expect, had no money, so I saw to it myself.

Fortuitously, my sister Jean had come up trumps. She produced an old post office savings book that I had inadvertently left behind under my mattress when I crept out of her house that fateful night to meet Sean, before heading for Luton. The ring cost me eight pounds. I had a few pounds left in the account to buy myself a small posy, and Jean held baby Jimmy throughout the ceremony.

My post office stamps also stretched to pay for what the priest insisted would be an invaluable introduction to being the wife of a Roman Catholic: I felt obliged to buy a white prayer book decorated with gold leaf, with additional notes on how to fulfil my wifely duties to allow my husband to follow his 'true faith'.

Hah! All the fun of the circus. We caught the bus back to our new home, the run-down terraced property on Manchester Old Road, calling in at the local pub on our way back so that Sean could down a pint of Manchester's best, whilst I silently raised a glass of port and lemonade to myself; I was going to need the very best of British luck, and more, if I was going to try to figure out a new plan of action. Then swiftly homewards, as we tore round to my sister's house next door to collect our baby boy.

Job done. No written invitations. No fancy clothes. No photographs. No reception. No honeymoon. Just a few obligatory comments about happiness from my parents through half-clenched teeth. And then there were none.

The house sat on one of the main roads coming out of Manchester in what comprised a run-down, post industrial area of the city. There were still some remaining small manufacturers in the area which provided piece work for local people. Demolitions had begun some years before and there were many empty sites where buildings once stood, leaving behind scatterings of bricks and rubble that told the tale of an industrious past.

Ours was an end terraced, back-to-back, Victorian house, with a living room that faced the street. Old net curtains that had seen better days hung by elastic at the front window, providing us with a modicum of privacy from the gawping of those who scurried along the street on their way to the nearby public house, or bus stop.

We were some of the lucky ones. We had an indoor toilet, unlike the rest of the back-to-backs whose tenants weren't spared the dash in all weathers to the pokey brick lavatories that stood in their back yards. However, despite the aforementioned 'modcon', the house itself was grim. High-ceilinged, damp, with dark interiors and a long, musty hall leading to a steep staircase, we realised, in our more optimistic moments, that it at least provided us with a roof over our heads. On bad days, we bemoaned the smelly, dingy, ill-maintained place as a relic of another era. We were just two, of thousands of people, who inhabited squalid places which belonged to another century, with little having been done to improve them since.

A newly emerging concept at that time, that environments and interiors affect our states of emotional well being, were the preserves of theorists and the aspiring classes, but in places like Openshaw the lack of Feng Shui had been wreaking savagery upon people's mental health since the industrial revolution.

Newly married, I don't think that either of us held great expectations of life there and neither, particularly, of our marriage. Sean was like a fish out of water. He needed to get a job and he spent the first few weeks looking for work on building sites where he might be able to be remunerated, cash-in-hand. However, conditions of employment on Manchester building sites seemed to be quite stringent in sharp contrast with his experiences in London.

I never *could* get to the bottom of why he had no Insurance Cards and appeared reluctant to apply to work legally in this country. He would dismiss the subject if I raised the issue, saying that he could always find some work without the 'trouble' of all that. However, his ability to find only casual work was a bone of contention from the start.

Initially, he would set off quite early, and be gone all day. Sometimes he would bring money home and at other times he would have nothing to show for it.

We lived from hand to mouth. I always had to ensure that, if there were no other provisions in the house, I would at least have baby formula to feed Jimmy. While he was very small and taking the bottle it was less of a problem but when I started to wean him I needed to ensure that we had enough of the small jars of Heinz baby food in the larder because we weren't able to eat regular, nutritious meals from which I could guarantee making a healthy pureed meal to feed my infant.

Days and weeks would pass when I saw and spoke to no-one, not even my sister and her husband and children who lived next door. They seemed to fare better than we did. Jean's husband, John, had a poorly paid job as a travelling salesman selling hats to retailers who held accounts with his firm. He wasn't very successful and didn't have the necessary drive or ruthlessness required to move new lines and, as a result, his commission was practically non-existent. His basic wage was at least regular, and Jean seemed somehow to make ends meet by undertaking part-time work as a cleaner in a local factory.

I always gleaned the impression that Sean was someone they preferred to steer well clear of.

As for our marriage it became, as I had expected, a union of convenience.

One particular day, Sean stated, moodily:

'I'm not going anywhere today.'

'Aren't you going to try to find *some* work? Anything at all?'

'There's no fucking work to be had for miles around.' I could see that he was becoming aggrieved about something.

I knew that there was plenty of work, if only he would register with the Department of Work and Pensions to obtain permission to work in this country. There were many Irish immigrants working in the north west of the country, especially in the Manchester and Liverpool areas.

I had begun to wonder, vaguely, if he had engaged in some illegitimate activity back home in Ireland that had landed him into trouble, and that he perhaps feared connections being made with criminal records back home, with possible police intervention.

Today he seemed unhappy and in some way defiant. I sensed trouble brewing.

'Look, I'm going to the shop to get some bread and some jars of soft food for Jimmy,' I said, lying baby in the pram and pushing my arms into my jacket. I needed to get out.

'Well, I hope you haven't got any of that fucking muck on your face!' he quipped. 'I don't want to see you wearing *any* makeup again. Do you understand me?'

'Sean, I've only got the tiniest bit of mascara on my lashes, and a dab of powder on my face,' pointing to my visage, as if to prove it.

'You don't need anything!' he said, his voice getting louder. 'Anyway, I know you. You'll be giving the fellas the glad eye, and they'll be wanting to take you down an alley to give you a good fucking. You'd like that, wouldn't you?' His anger was at boiling point and I couldn't understand any of it. The old green monster was rearing its head again, threatening to cause trouble.

Jimmy was beginning to stir in the pram, but I felt that I had to try to assuage Sean's insecurities, and calm him; assure him that he was the only one I wanted to give the 'glad eye' to, as he had put it; this 'jack-in-the-box', paranoid jealousy which I frequently had to try to suppress.

'Look, Sean, I'm wearing a ring. I have a child with me. What's more, there aren't any men around. They're all at work! And even if the shop was *filled* with men I'm married to *you*.' As if to ratify my assurances I added: 'Why don't you come with me?'

'I'm not going anywhere,' he said, and lit up a cigarette, pushing aside the net curtain and staring out at the dismal main road as if there was anything to look at except the derelict, boarded-up buildings on the other side.

Tension was never far away. I stepped out into the cold, wintry urban landscape, glad to be breathing in the muck of the main road than the sickening, suffocating air indoors.

I pushed Jimmy up to the corner shop, wishing I could extend my shopping trip to a walk around several blocks, or up to the little park about fifteen minutes walk away, but I knew only too well that if I did, I would risk a greater inquisition when I returned. I was on a timer, and it gave rise to a nervous sprint there and back.

I was always anxious, frightened of a flare up of his irrational temper, and frequently feeling as if I was walking on eggshells to avoid upsetting him.

Gone were the loving proclamations. Sean was struggling with an alien landscape and with not being able to enjoy the 'craic', and a good few pints of Guinness. Also, he had the added pressure of needing to bring in enough money to pay the rent, for the electricity meter and to buy food for the three of us.

Little did I realise, but he had a new scheme up his sleeve which he intended would give him a night life, in addition to earning potential.

When I returned he had dropped his jealous line of attack. I was relieved. I blabbered on about there being none of the bread we liked and having to buy another sort of loaf. My banal utterances were deliberate, as if to illustrate a preoccupation with domestic minutiae in which there was no place for sexual dalliances.

'Anyway, I've decided,' he said, right out of the blue, 'I'm going out tonight. I might be able to strike a few deals.'

I didn't like the sound of this, but I wasn't in a position to oppose him.

'What sort of deals? Where are you going?'

'Don't you worry. I'm just going to try to meet up with a few fellas. Maybe there's some evening work to be had in town, you know, cash in hand. I might try some of the pubs and clubs.'

At one-thirty in the morning I heard the key turning in the lock of the front door. When he came into the bedroom it was obvious that he had been drinking. He reached deep into his pocket and threw a wad of notes on to the bed. I sat up and counted them.

'Where did you get all this? Did you earn this?' I couldn't believe it. There was enough money to keep us going for the rest of the week, with a visit to the launderette, some shopping, and more. 'What did you do?'

'I was taken on in a restaurant not far from Piccadilly. I've been up to my arms in soap suds all evening!' he said, laughing. 'The washer-upper hadn't turned up, and so they had me in the kitchen, scrubbing all sorts of pots, pans and dishes.'

That didn't account for the alcohol on his breath or his glassy eyes, I thought, and he must have sensed my mistrust, as he continued:

'After the restaurant closed the fella who owned it took a few of us into the back of a pub nearby. It was well after closing time but nobody gave a fuck,' he said. 'He's a good sort and bought us all a round of drinks. And also, get this: the landlord of the pub saw me admiring an axe that was by the fire, you know, for decoration. He said he had two of 'em and I could have the one with the red handle if I wanted it. It's downstairs. Go and take a look.'

'An axe! What do we need an axe for? We have a coal fire,' I said.

'It looks really good. Just for show, you know.'

It all seemed plausible, other than the idea of Sean washing up! This man, who never lifted a finger to wash so much as a cup, was now a restaurant's hired dishwasher! As for the axe, I found it incredible that he'd carried that home on the bus, and I could think of far better ways of decorating the fireplace than having an axe propped up for fun. Some more coal and a box of matches might have been a good start. Notwithstanding that, he seemed happy, and as for his explanation of work, I just had to live with it. At least for the time being.

A regular pattern emerged. He seemed to get work nightly, and was paid cash-in-hand. A few weeks later he told me that he'd been taken on in a club as a bouncer. I lay in bed, night after night, waiting to hear the door, never knowing what time he would return, or what sort of mood he was in.

During the day he would stay in bed, sometimes until the early afternoon. I would be up early, as usual, seeing to Jimmy, busying myself around the house, and going shopping.

On one particular occasion Sean woke up in a foul mood. He had drank too much the night before. He started shouting obscenities at me, and accusing me of having a lover in the house when he was out during the evening.

'You're fucking me around, aren't you?'

My attempts to diffuse this tirade of abuse weren't working.

'Right,' he said, 'take your clothes off. Now!'

'Don't be ridiculous,' I said, trying to get past him to go into the kitchen to turn off the kettle on the stove to prepare little Jimmy's feed.

He jumped up and grabbed hold of the axe.

I suddenly realised that he wasn't joking. I froze as he pushed me against the wall and held the head of the axe to my cheek.

'Sean, don't, please. What are you doing?'

The blade of the axe was cold against my face.

'I could make a real mess of you with this,' he threatened, 'now take off your clothes!'

Jimmy was crying for his next feed, and he might have been frightened by Sean's raised voice. I slowly undressed, distraught and frightened, folding my clothes and placing them on to the couch.

'Now go and turn that fucking kettle off and get back in here,' he instructed. I knew that anything I said might further incite his volatility, and all of a sudden I wasn't sure whether I knew this man standing in front of me any more.

'Okay,' I murmured. Minutes later, completely naked, and trembling, I swept up my precious baby into my arms and wiped his wet cheeks, holding him to my breast, and slowly walked into the kitchen to turn off the hob.

Sean stood, wielding the axe, smiling. He was taking sadistic pleasure in watching me, frightened, and obedient.

This was an exercise in humiliation. He was bright enough to know that if he were to inflict any serious injury upon me it would rebound on his life forever.

I stood for what seemed like an eternity, rocking Jimmy in my arms for so long until his little body fell asleep again, without having had his feed. I could bear the humiliation, the ridicule. But the overwhelming distress I experienced at not being able to feed my baby boy was something which was painful beyond measure. How I managed to keep rocking his little body until, finally, he was asleep again, I'll never know. It took so much out of me, and the agony was beyond anything I had personally suffered at the hands of this man. I couldn't bear to deny my own baby his food. This was the cruellest thing Sean had ever done.

When Sean had achieved his adrenalin-fuelled power kick, and after ridiculing my body, telling me how he hated my body, and how much he preferred big, busty, curvaceous women than women like me, he suddenly stopped and caught sight of the time, saying he needed to get washed and changed. There was an abrupt end to my purgatory. He hurried upstairs, and I quickly got dressed again and made up Jimmy's feed. When Sean came down, looking smart and dapper, and adjusting his tie, I was sitting on the couch, as Jimmy was burping and staring into my eyes, happy again.

I waited until long after Sean had left, and dressed my baby in warm clothes and swaddled him in the yellow blanket, before walking out into the dark January evening to the telephone box up the main road. I lifted the receiver and dialled The Samaritans. I was desperate to talk to someone. I spoke to a kindly-sounding, gently-spoken man and told him all that had happened earlier that afternoon. I gasped for breath as I cried and spluttered, relating the whole dreadful experience.

He listened, and there were long silences. He expressed how sorry he felt for me. And, how did I now feel about this, he asked. What did I want to do about this? Did I think it might happen again?

Fifteen minutes passed. It was futile. He was a long way away. This was my hell, *right here, and now*. I had nowhere to go, no one to turn to; the same old problem. I thanked him for listening and I walked back in the rain to the place I now hated, and wanted to leave.

I must be so ugly to him, I despaired. I looked dowdy. My clothes were from jumble sales. I was growing thinner by the week with an anxiety that was constant.

When Sean returned in the early hours of the next morning he appeared to be in ludicrously good spirits. It was as if the cruel incident had never happened.

'Here,' he said, throwing the night's wad of notes on to the bed. I was aware that he withheld some of each night's money for his own drinking binges, but I was past caring, just so long as we had enough to live on while, in the meantime, I had to try to work out how I could manage to move on.

Then he dropped a bombshell.

'I can get more money doing what I'm doing now, than in any regular work,' he boasted, deliberately letting something big slip.

'What's that supposed to mean? Aren't you earning it doing some sort of work in a club in town?'

'No,' he spewed. 'It's easier to lead those sick bastards up an alleyway or even go back with them to their grotty lodgings and, then, just as they're dropping their trousers I roll them.'

'Oh my God!' I shrieked in shock, 'what does 'roll' mean? Do you mean you hit them?'

'Not necessarily. Sometimes, I just have to threaten them. They know I'm fit, and capable of doing real damage to them, and sometimes they just tell me to take some money from their wallets. At other times, they say they're going to call the police, but I don't give those dirty bastards the chance. Usually it takes just one punch. But sometimes only a threat, and they give me some money to disappear.'

'Sean! That's grievance bodily harm. It's blackmail. You're committing terrible offences! You'll end up behind bars. But apart from that, it's immoral; it's cruel. What have they ever done to you? Nothing!'

'They only fucking fancy me, that's what! They want to give me one up my arse! Either that or they want *me* to give *them* one! The dirty perverts. The fucking sick bastards! They deserve what they get! They definitely deserve to pay for soliciting me!'

'But aren't you soliciting *them*?'

'They deserve nothing less than they get. Take my word.'

'So now you're judge and jury, for a handsome stolen fee.' I felt aghast. Sickened, by this revelation. 'How do you know you're not catching diseases anyway?'

The AIDS and HIV epidemic had yet to arise, but I was thinking about the other venereal diseases that I'd learned about. I was horrified at what had been going on nightly, right under my nose, and I'd known nothing about it.

For quite a time I had been suspicious of his movements. His so-called income was too predictable, too generous to be from so many business concerns prepared to operate illegally. I had no doubt that there *were* some business owners who were happy to pay cash-in-hand to evade tax but, surely, not every night.

I felt ashamed. I felt sorry for those men.

Just over a year before, the Sexual Offences Act of 1967 permitted homosexual acts between consenting adults over the age of twenty one. Many people in the UK regarded this piece of legislation with abhorrence. Homosexuality between males was still considered by many to be a deviance, and something for which men should obtain 'treatment' to redress. However, for many practising homosexuals the Act symbolised new freedoms for them in which to seek openly transparent encounters, and there occurred a surge of sexual incidents, especially in town centres, in toilets and areas where men would loiter.

I couldn't sleep that night. Sean slept like a log.

I tossed and turned. How much of what he said was actually true, I wondered. Or did he actually *engage* in the sexual acts in order to be paid the fee, just like a male prostitute? Or a 'rent boy' as the new term was coined.

He protested that there was no way that he would *ever* want to have sexual relations with a male. I tended to believe him because he was so convincing in his expression of revulsion, and outrage, at the idea of men engaging in anal sex with each other.

Things were beginning to add up. Only two weeks before, I had discovered an embarrassing, personal condition about which I had agonised, and for which I knew that I needed to get some help. I finally plucked up enough courage to visit the GP. He confirmed a diagnosis of pubic lice, commonly known as 'crabs'. He prescribed a lotion which I had to apply, twice daily. He didn't ask any questions or cast doubt upon my relationship or where one of us might have contracted them, and I thought that this was odd. It left me wondering whether, in a depressed area like Openshaw many of his other patients had consulted him with the same embarrassing problem.

It was only now occurring to me that Sean had caught them from one of these men, and passed them on to me. It was a source of great shame, and it weighed heavily upon me, as both of us were treated. Furthermore, it also served to consolidate serious questions as to my husband's fidelity and his preoccupation with preying on vulnerable men who wanted to pay for sex.

It was hard to make sense of what was happening. In my mind, Sean was becoming subsumed into an underworld of people and behaviours that seemed incredible and shocking to me.

Although we had only been married for four months our own sexual relationship was far from what one might expect. When Sean was at his unhappiest and cruellest he would demand sex. There was no consideration given to me. Afterwards he would say things like:

'There, now I've made you pregnant again. I hope you'll be lumbered for a second time.' Or, 'I have to think of other women now while I'm fucking you, you are so fucking ugly.'

I was at my lowest point. I was merely existing. I was depressed, and permanently anxious. I felt, quite seriously, at times, that life was not worth living. But I loved my dear little baby boy so much, and I knew how much he needed me. I also knew what would happen if I were not there to take care of him. The thought was unbearable, and it was always for the love of Jimmy that I felt I had to keep going somehow.

I couldn't share any of this with any other living soul. I was so deeply ashamed of everything that I couldn't even confide in my sister, next door. Besides, they had their lives to get on with, and Jean and I weren't so close as to even begin to tell her *half* of the horrendous existence through which I was living.

CHAPTER 11

Surprisingly, at times, Sean appeared to be more contrite. He became kinder to me, and very loving towards little Jimmy. It became more noticeable around the time that there appeared to be some sort of a breakthrough into a more settled existence for Sean.

One day he explained, happily, that he had met a young businessman, a kind Christian gentleman called David, at a bar in Manchester. David was about to be married, and lived in the country, not far from Glossop. He had apparently bought a large old country house in which he intended that he and his bride would live after they had married.

'You'll have to meet David sometime, Sean said. He's a really nice man.'

Relations between us seemed to be changing slightly for the better. He told me a little about David and his life and business. He wanted Sean to go to his house to estimate some work that needed doing, to see if he could undertake what David described initially as 'rather extensive painting, indoors and outdoors'. He also wanted him to do some other outdoor work: pointing, and work on the guttering and roof, and there was a fair amount of garden maintenance work to be done in the two acre sized plot, in readiness for his new bride, who apparently wanted to create a rose garden.

Sean said that he was planning to go at the weekend. Glossop was a distance away, and David's house would be complicated to reach by public transport and so David had suggested that they meet up in town and he would drive him to his new house. He could stay over to meet his fiancée, then spend some time estimating the extent of the work to be done, and be dropped off in town again on Sunday evening.

'What do you think?' he queried. I knew that he wasn't seeking my approval. His mind was already made up.

From what Sean had described, this man seemed to be a good person, and I reflected that he might prove to be a positive influence upon him, heralding a change which might just set Sean on to a better path. And, who knows, I thought, if Sean could pull off these jobs successfully, he might be capable, eventually, of setting up his own property maintenance business and making a real go of it.

Sean packed a small bag and set off to meet him on Friday evening.

His departure spelled the start of a short period of respite: two whole days in which there was no one from whom I had to watch my guard, no one to humour, to wait up for in the early hours of the morning worse for wear; wondering what was going to be said; which stories to believe and which to discount. It was bliss. Just me and my darling baby whose development I could observe and enjoy, and with whom I could interact, without having to stop abruptly to provide for the selfish demands of a bully.

Later on Sunday evening he returned, full of news regarding David's property, and telling me about the plan of work they had drawn up between them. Sean seemed to be on cloud nine. He

187

said that he might have found his niche, at long last. Furthermore, he said that he had actually made a good start on clearing out an old outbuilding, and he enthused about how he was going to make it a wonderful workroom for David's fiancee, Lucille, who liked experimenting with textile art activities in her spare time. What a woman, I thought. And does she realise how fortunate she is?

'So what's Lucille like?' I enquired, with genuine interest.

'Oh, unfortunately I didn't get to meet her, after all. She works for Granada TV and she has a studio flat at Salford Quays where she stays when she's tied up with a production.'

'Oh, that's a shame,' I said. 'Having heard all about David I think it would have been good for you to meet her.'

'I did see a photo of her, though,' he said. 'She looks very nice. Very middle class, I suppose. But then, look at David, he's obviously had a good start in life, but he treats me as if we're best buddies. He's very respectful. You'd never know that he was so rich. His company is one of the fastest growing businesses in the north west, and he employs hundreds of people.'

Sean seemed happy. He put a roll of notes on the table.

'There's two hundred pounds there!' he said proudly.

'What? You're kidding!' I exclaimed. 'What was that for? Has he more money than sense?' I couldn't believe this. In the late nineteen sixties that amount of money represented a fortune for us.

'He's so used to contractors messing him around, not turning up and overcharging for work. I think he wanted to show me that if I didn't let him down he'd look after me. I think our luck is about to change, Sue,' he said, breaking into a silly dance around the room, flinging notes about, as if he hadn't a care.

'Don't, I said, you'll lose them,' and we scrabbled around, giggling, snatching at the notes and counting the money in earnest, before putting it back on the table. Moments like this were like fleeting wisps of gold dust, reminding me of the side of Sean I once knew, and fell in love with. Happy, silly moments when we would end up with our arms around each other, loving and sharing simple, special times together.

There followed some days and weeks when Sean seemed to be much more contented. He would frequently joke with me; we would take walks out together pushing Jimmy in his pram to some of the public parks and green spaces, away from the seedy areas of Openshaw. There were even instances when he would promise me a better life to come. I didn't bother daring to hope.

Sean was far from being an intrinsically 'bad guy'. He had learned bad ways. A life of poverty, of harsh authorities, of beatings, and years of learning to get by, doing whatever it takes, had led him into dens of iniquity. I never really thought that he was actively choosing to live like this. We had shared so many conversations about his wanting to go back to Ireland one day. Despite the austerity of his younger life, and also because the country lagged far behind ours in its development he had described communities and kinship that represented a rockbed of safety, love and support, at a time long after many of our own communities in the UK had begun to disintegrate and disperse.

Moreover, I understood, fully, Sean's refusal to conform. Not for a moment did I condone it, but I knew, despite everything, that he was flailing about in an alienating world which he didn't truly understand, or engage with, and in which he had no chance of being able to sustain happily within. His take on his circumstances would have been the antithesis of 'if you can't beat 'em, join 'em.' That is to say, in knowing that he was barred from joining a 'club' he would deal with it by going in fighting. He would attack first, before he 'got his teeth kicked in'. His insufficient schooling due to years of absconding to avoid beatings, only to get more; the prejudice and the language discrimination here in England which, in a single utterance alone, judged him as a dim-witted Irish man when he was anything *but*, coupled with blatant racism in the UK at that time illustrated that he, and many of his fellow citizens, weren't wanted here, except only to do the back-breaking jobs of labouring, building the roads and all the other work that our native population wasn't inclined to want to do. Then they must go back home. Isn't that the same with all instances of immigration? A country doesn't want outsiders, but it needs their labour; then there follows economic growth, but accompanied by social unrest.

More visits to David's house followed. Sean went for three weekends, and four more separate visits of one week's duration. Each time he returned he would tell me of all the work that he'd undertaken, and how pleased David had been. Sean seemed to be enamoured with David. He talked of his fine clothes, his excellent taste, his gentle demeanour and his kindly humour and good company. He still hadn't met Lucille. And money continued to drip into our household, intermittently, followed by periods of Sean sitting on his hands until the next time.

I began to feel increasingly uneasy about Sean's work absences. In these years, which embraced the gradual beginnings of what we may now regard as a sexual revolution in our society, we were less accustomed to hearing about changes in sexual orientation and sexual behaviours which, if they were in evidence before, were kept strictly private. There was no Gay Pride, for instance, no 'trans movement,' and men and women were expected to follow traditional paths into marriage and heterosexual relationships. But Lucille's continued absence, and other concerns I had fed my imagination and made me privately suspicious.

Sean informed me that David was about to embark on a business trip to the Philippines where he was opening a new office, and it was likely to be another four weeks or so before he could return to David's house to undertake more of the important work.

'Isn't it possible for you to work there in his absence?' I asked.

'No, there are only a few cleaners who come and go, and he'd prefer to at least pop in and out to provide specifications for the jobs, and approve the work. Look, I just have to be patient. At least there'll be plenty of work for me when he comes back.'

Over five weeks had passed and there was still no word yet from David. Sean telephoned the house a few times and each time the cleaners seemed to be able to tell him nothing. During this period Sean returned to his night time stints. He assured me that he was now doing 'proper work', but I knew that I couldn't ever trust him to tell the truth.

Though things seemed more settled in some respects, life was far from normal. I lived on a knife edge, not knowing what to expect each day. Then, one evening when Sean was about to go out, he embarked into another angry tirade, which masqueraded as a warning that if he ever discovered that a man had been in the house when he was out he would not be responsible for his actions when he returned. The whole thing was ludicrous. Conjured up from his sad imagination. What was going on in his head? Did he operate in such a corrupt underworld that he truly believed that *I* would ever behave so flagrantly disingenuously? My usual lines of reassurances and appeasement were now old hat, and I felt ground down under the weight of being accused once more of things that were unthinkable.

The door slammed hard as Sean left the house. Something this time, deep inside me, finally snapped. I didn't want to face whatever mood he brought home with him. This time I felt that I had hit rock bottom. I couldn't cope any more with the fear of worrying about what I might have to try to combat later on.

I wrapped Jimmy warmly and set off for the telephone box. The Samaritan sounded to be a middle aged lady who listened very attentively, as I wept, and told of my fears, of whether we would be harmed when Sean returned, and even about having to contend with his bad moods and give in to his bullying, sexual demands. I cried that I was trapped. I had no where to go, and explained that although my sister and her husband lived next door, and my parents lived not that far away, neither party would not be able to cope with Sean or the reality of my life with him.

She urged me not to discount them entirely; to try my parents first, and ask them outright for temporary refuge, giving them the reasons why, in a palatable format, in order for them to understand my need to get out of the house. If that didn't work, she asked me to consider seeking refuge next door.

I stood in the phone box, deliberating over what I should do. My brother-in-law, John, had what I felt to be a delicate disposition. His sister had recently died, aged twenty one, from what was then a little understood neurological illness. He found day-to-day-life itself hard enough to cope with, and I couldn't imagine involving him in my need to flee the house. Furthermore Jean wouldn't have taken kindly to me sleeping there either. She now had two small sons, and spare room in the house was tight. Apart from that, I feared that it would be Sean's first port of call. That just wouldn't be fair on them, I reflected.

I decided to take the bull by the horns again and telephone my father. My parents were currently renting another property, a small cottage on the outskirts of Ashton-Under-Lyne, as they were still uncertain about their next, permanent move.

Dad answered the telephone.

'It's Susan.' I took a deep breath. 'Look, Dad, I don't know how to say this, but, this marriage isn't working. Sean's gone out for the evening and I'm dreading what will happen when he returns.'

There was a pause. 'Are you saying that you're concerned for your safety, and Jimmy's too?' he asked, solemnly.

'Yes, I am. He drinks too much and I get frightened.' I was amazed that he hadn't dismissed me, out of hand. This was the man who had also dished out slaps, and been guilty of aggressive, bullying behaviour towards me. Or had he had enough time to rethink his past errors, and now regretted them? Something told me that he already knew that our marriage was faltering. It was possible that Jean had heard Sean's raised voice, or the slamming of the door at night, and had told Mum about it.

'Right.' he said, resolvedly. 'I'm going to come down in a taxi, and you must be ready with the baby to hop in. No messing about. Lock the front door and get into the taxi right away.'

I was taken by surprise at his response, but never more grateful.

Half an hour later there was a knock at the door and Dad accompanied me, with baby Jimmy and my bag of baby food and nappies, to the waiting taxi. In the back of the cab Dad said:

'I think that you should cut your losses, Susan.' He repeated this phrase later that evening, as if it were a well rehearsed cliché of advice he had been considering dispensing for some time.

I didn't say it but, though comments like that made good sense, they were impracticable. Sean would never agree to me going *anywhere*. He would find me, and object in the only way he knew how to. And even if it *was* possible to make a break for it, I would be back at square one. Married though I was, I would be classed as a single parent and as such prevented from obtaining somewhere to live. Or did he think that *Sean* would actually leave if I asked him to? For my headstrong husband to be persuaded to go *anywhere* there would have to be something in it for him.

In my parents' tiny cottage, one of the two upstairs bedrooms was occupied by themselves and, in the other, my younger sister, Kay. Dad said that I could sleep in an armchair, with my legs resting on a footstool. There was no couch. I nevertheless felt grateful for this temporary refuge and the peace of mind it brought.

Because Jimmy was teething, we both had a restless night in which I paced up and down the living room floor, rocking him to and fro, for what seemed like an eternity. Eventually, around four o'clock in the morning I fell into an exhausted sleep. I was no further forward about how I could move onwards, other than an idea I'd had of somehow contacting the Citizen's Advice Bureau to ask for any practical help they may be able to give. However, just being able to access the Bureau would be a feat in itself because Sean was always around during the daytime.

I was awoken abruptly by a knocking on the front door at around six o'clock in the morning. My father came downstairs. He must have known that there was only one person who would come calling at that time.

I could only hear smatterings of the conversation. Though far from cordial, it appeared to be a reasonably non-confrontational exchange in which my father seemed to carry off the deception that I was not in their house. Sean persisted, as only *I* knew he would. He wanted to come in to check. My father held his ground. Sean was agitated, but did not lose his temper. He was probably at the stage of sobering up. My father asked him why I would have left the house at night anyway, but Sean was not taking the bait. The meeting ended with Dad saying that the only thing he could suggest, was that I had gone to Droylsden to stay at a friend's house. It was where I had gone to school and I would have been able to travel there easily by bus. Most of my old school friends still lived there. Sean left dissatisfied, but I was thankful that all hell didn't break loose.

Little did I realise it at that time, but mayhem *had* already erupted a couple of hours previously, not long after Sean arrived home only to discover that we weren't in the house. He promptly went round to my sister's house where he woke up the family and confronted my brother-in-law at their front door. Sean wouldn't hear of John's denial that I was not sheltering inside, and he forced his way indoors, attacking John and man-handling him almost the full length of the hall in his bid to try to find me. Once satisfied that I wasn't there, he pressurised John into giving him my parents' address so that he could try to find me there.

I had wondered how he had found out where Mum and Dad lived. It wasn't something that *I* had ever told him, and although I knew the address I had never been there before either, and nor, of course, had we ever been invited.

In the tiny cottage kitchen where Mum and Dad came down for breakfast, and with all of us having had very little sleep, I came to the decision that I couldn't risk putting my parents through more trouble by staying any longer. Also, the little sleep I had managed to snatch was not the most comfortable, sitting almost bolt upright in one of the high-backed, fireside chairs. I decided, therefore, with the dawning of the day, that I had to try, somehow, to talk to Sean about our relationship. I wondered whether I could include some incentives for *him* especially, that would help to provide us both with some time apart.

Staying at Mum and Dad's hadn't been in vain, however. It had provided me with the briefest respite in which I was able to stand back from all the strife in which we were living, to regroup my thoughts and gather courage.

I waited until an appropriate time when I knew that Sean would have had some rest, and not still feeling the effects of drink, and I returned home with our baby to face whatever lay ahead.

The very fact that I had chosen to stay elsewhere, and had actually *found somewhere else to go,* away from under his control, had unnerved Sean. It had been a gamble that paid off, although I hadn't initially thought of it in this respect.

He greeted me with a rush of relief.

'Sue, where the hell have you been? I've been worried sick. I thought you'd left me for good. Sue, please, come here.' He threw his arms around me and Jimmy. He had been crying.

'I stayed with my friend, Carol, at her Mum's house.'

'Who the fuck is Carol? And where does *she* live?'

She lives in Droylsden. She's still in the house in which she grew up, and where I spent many happy times when I was little, playing and visiting her. I have told you about her. She was my closest, dearest friend.'

'Your father *said* you might be in Droylsden.'

'You saw Dad? When did you see him?' I said, feigning ignorance of his early morning visit.

'It doesn't matter, now. You're back, and that's all that matters. Come here, now.' He hugged me, and held me close to him. Grasping the moment, if ever there was going to be a good time to talk seriously about our future it had to be now.

'Look, why don't I make a cup of tea. I bought these biscuits in the Co-op in Droylsden, and we can sit down and have a talk.'

'What about?' he said, quizzically. At least he was still smiling, so glad he was to see me back.

After feeding Jimmy another bottle of formula and a little pureed pear I settled him in his cot. I knew that he would finally give in to sleep after a restless night of teething. Sean and I sat down together.

He immediately confessed to having been physically aggressive towards my brother-in-law, John, during the early hours of the morning. I was mortified.

'You didn't hurt him, did you?' I asked, in alarm.

'I just roughed him up a bit, that's all.'

I sensed it was more than that. John was of slight build and nervous disposition.

'Did you punch him? Did you strike a blow?'

'Well, nothing massive, you know, I got hold of him and pushed him down the hall, that's all. He survived alright, because he got up and I said I just wanted to know where you were, and that I wanted to take a look inside because I thought they were hiding you.'

'Look, Sean, if you thought I'd be in hiding, then I would have to be hiding from *you*, and for some good reason.' I paused for a moment. 'If that's the case, then that doesn't sound like a good recipe for our marriage. Does it to you?'

'Sue, you know full well that every married couple has their ups and downs. God, me mammy and daddy fucking fight all the time and they still ended up having eleven kids,' he said, laughing. 'And with the two that died there'd have been thirteen of us.' Anyway, why *did* you take off like that?'

'I think you can work that one out. Look, Sean, in your heart you must know that I'm not unfaithful. That I'd not look at anyone else. You're constantly accusing me of messing around. It's unfair and cruel. I can't cope with it. Things are tough enough as it is.'

'I know, Sue. I'm sorry. I am. I'll make it up to you, I promise. I don't know what gets into me.'

'But it's much more than that, though,' I said, thinking how to broach his so-called 'work', all the spurious, illegal activity of his twilight world, and his disappearing in the evenings until the early hours the next day.

'I don't like the way we're living. I'm not talking necessarily about this house in this God-forsaken area. I can just about cope with that, so long as it's not forever, but it's everything else. I don't like the fact that you don't have a regular day job. It's not normal to obtain money the way you're doing. No marriage could possibly survive this way of living.'

'Do you think that *I'm* happy, living this way?' he said, and I watched the way his eyes looked down. Suddenly I could see the child in him.

'I've spent me life flying by the seat of me pants, literally!' He laughed at the double entendre.

I wiped a tear away from my eye.

'It's not funny,' I said.

'I'm fucking useless, aren't I. I'm no good to you, Sue, he wailed.' His transparency took me by surprise.

'I have an idea, Sean. Please, just listen while I suggest something. Hear me out first, before you say anything; and don't get angry, and start shouting and tearing into me.'

'I promise, I won't,' he answered.

'We can't go on like this. Neither of us is happy. It's not fair on our little boy, either. He deserves so much more from his parents.' I spoke slowly, and in a measured way; I didn't want to put my foot in it, or say anything that might result in plunging us even further back into the abyss of our relationship.

'Look, I know that you're missing home, and that you've not seen you parents or your family for a long time. Why don't you go back, just for a while, or as long as you feel you'd like to? You could take stock of things, and we'll stay in touch, writing each week.'

'Jesus, Sue, how long are you expecting me to stay back there?'

I paused. 'I suppose, for as long as you feel you need to clear your head. To decide to stop all the stuff that's been going on. Until you feel you can live a straight, honest life for the sake of the three of us. As long as it takes, Sean. I can't take living like this any more.'

He went quiet.

'For what it's worth, I don't like living like this either,' he admitted, pathetically, and fell silent again. 'I'll need to ring David. I forgot to tell you that he's back from the Philippines and he wants me to carry on with the work in Glossop.'

It didn't surprise me that he had he had conveniently forgotten to tell me that bit of news. But I acceded to what I knew wouldn't simply involve a telephone call. No, he would need to go and see him. And, like a slow drip I was beginning to crystallise a clearer picture of what I was convinced was more than a working relationship. Also Sean would no doubt need more money to go to Ireland, and enough to give some to his family, and David was the man who could be relied upon to provide it. So, the question burned in my head, was Sean providing a range of services, including those of a more intimate nature?

'I'm sure that he'd be upset to think I'd left him high and dry with only half of the house painted. I could try to decorate a few more rooms for him this weekend, and let him know my plans, in the short term. After all, he knows we don't have a telephone where he can reach me, and it's only fair.'

Even now, I thought, he's lying. He's living a double life. Why would a man keep throwing large amounts of money at Sean for work that can be sourced locally, for a fraction of the cost that he was paying. I only hoped that Sean wasn't blackmailing him. David seemed to want him to be there, and Sean seemed happy when he returned from his visits, and full of admiration for this man. I could only surmise that, despite David's impending marriage, his duplicitous sexual inclinations included a proclivity towards the same sex.

If a final visit to see David meant that Sean would return to Ireland, then so be it, I thought. I was treading nervously on eggshells.

Sean came back home on the following Monday. He placed some money on the table, and tearfully he said:

'I'm going to keep going, Sue. Whatever you think of me I do, honestly, love you. And I love my baby, too.'

The sad thing was, I knew that he did. I also knew that this moment might represent the culmination of the last vestiges of our relationship.

'I'll write you, Sue. Please write back. You've got the address.' I nodded. He quickly grabbed hold of me and held me tightly, close to him.

'Bye, my darling Sue,' he wept. 'I'm so sorry for everything.' And he turned and hurried out of the door and into the busy street where the sun streamed in through our musty, miserable hallway.

I sat down and wailed. In agonising, tortuous despair; in relief; and in sorrow. All I wanted was a normal life, free from lies, anger and fear.

Besides, I now had a new problem to face: I had missed two periods.

CHAPTER 12

With Sean gone, I spent the next two days sleeping when Jimmy slept. With a brand new tooth pushing through his bottom gum at the front, and another next to it threatening to sprout soon, like all babies at this stage of development, he was tearful and, at times, inconsolable. When restful sleep finally came his way, I slept too, whatever the hour.

Being able to adopt my baby's rhythms was, in many senses, restorative for me. Did nature intend that to happen, but in today's world with its practical demands and distracting interventions we are robbed of its pleasures and inherent benefits? If only we could all live more naturally and be able to ignore the demands and dictates of interlopers, I mused, life would surely be more harmonious.

I devoted all of my time to Jimmy's well being. I played with him, observed his interactions with his environment; his behaviours, the gnawing at everything he picked up. I watched him happily banging spoons together on the table, marvelling at his ability to enjoy and control the sounds and reverberations. I took him out for long walks, and lifted him out of the pram to see the sights and sounds of the greener and less oppressive parts of Openshaw. We listened to a blackbird's joyous song and watched pigeons fly to our feet as I sprinkled breadcrumbs around us.

Five months old, he was engaging with the world and expressing a multitude of different sounds about how he felt about it. I observed every detail, every nuance of my baby boy's development, and talked to him about everything with which he engaged. I found myself enjoying, more so than ever, our walks out and our playtimes together. Even mealtimes were a joy as he searched into my eyes for my smile, my words and my love. I sang to both of my babies, my living child and my unborn baby, for now there was a new life, immersing itself into the sounds and sensations of its new home.

The housework was left almost entirely, other than the immediate imperatives of preparing food, clearing dishes, and washing interminable nappies. The only household task which I did attend to was getting rid of the axe. I wrapped it in bundles of newspaper, put it into a large, used postal bag and dropped it into the old metal dustbin in the back yard amidst other rubbish intended for landfill.

I made an appointment with my local GP and took a urine sample with me. Pregnancy tests were not yet on the market. Although I *knew* that I had conceived again I needed to have clinical confirmation of my pregnancy and an estimated due date. After taking blood, he said that I should make another appointment for a week's time when he would have the results.

Here was the same cheerless doctor who had previously diagnosed my embarrassing complaint, and I could only imagine that he took a dim view of patients like me; nineteen years old, with a second child on the way, with what he may have thought was no mind to do anything else, like the rest of the lumpen classes, but to emulate rabbits all day; and if we weren't busy procreating the next generation of layabouts we'd be spreading parasites and other unwanted pathogens.

But what little does he know. Already I had a new plan. It was far reaching, and embraced a vision for a future elsewhere. I didn't know quite where yet, but only that there *was* a beautiful world out there, way beyond Openshaw. I had dreams.

I started to hope for a better life again. The new arrival would be welcomed into my world with as much love and anticipation as the first. However, this would be my second, and last, child, I determined. The pill was becoming more widely prescribed for married women and I knew that I would probably be able obtain it. Only time would tell, though, whether I would actually need it, depending upon whether or not Sean had left for good.

The pill was first introduced into the UK in the early nineteen sixties when it was announced that married women who wished to use the contraceptive would be able to access it. In practice, for some years to come, contraception advice was only given to older married women who no longer wanted any children or whose health was at serious risk in having another child. However, in 1967 the NHS Family Planning Act was passed and it was widely recognised that unwanted children in low income households caused significant financial pressure for such families, and so it became more widely available on the NHS.

I had already worked out that my new baby would be born approximately twelve months after Jimmy's birth, and it meant that my little ones could grow up together, while I was young, and fit, and had the energy and vision to give them a good life in our shared journey. Despite all the ills that had beset my path so far I always felt that, beyond our day-to-day existence, longer term adventures lay ahead; ones which I would make count. Wholeheartedly, therefore, I began to embrace the idea of having not one, but two children. Having had the luxury of rest and contemplation, I felt very happy at the prospect.

I was beginning to feel freer, more relaxed and open to greater future possibilities.

By contrast also, and especially when night time fell, I felt extremely lonely. There had been no word from Mum and Dad. I wasn't surprised. They wouldn't have wanted to interfere with whatever followed that recent, stressful evening. And neither would they regard Sean in any favourable light, even though I had disclosed very little of how we had been living. They had probably resigned themselves to the idea that their daughter had fallen prey to a man for whom they had no respect and nor did they want to try to get to know.

Jean and John next door were too preoccupied with their own difficulties and hardships to want to bother to make regular contact with me. Besides, Sean's impetuous and unwarranted actions in their home put paid to any improved relations I might otherwise have had with them, especially if they had known that Sean had returned to Ireland. But they didn't. No-one knew.

In the second week following Sean's departure I found the local library, and joined it. I borrowed two books for myself and three big picture books for Jimmy. Life was far from sweet, but it was getting better each day.

I received a letter from Eire, as Sean had promised. It was short, saying how he hoped that I was managing okay, and that he was missing me and Jimmy. He wrote a telling couple of his lines in which he expressed that he had forgotten how much slower and lovelier life was in the country of his birth. I knew that Sean's parents would be overjoyed to see him, and I wondered what he had told them about his working life. They would believe him, of course, and probably make all the wrong assumptions that money was plentiful, and deduce that he must be doing well for himself, and doing right by us too.

From what Sean had told me I knew that all of his younger siblings adored him. To them, he was the joker, the happy-go-lucky rogue who breezed in and out of their lives. His good looks, his charm and playfulness were what had beguiled me too in the early days of our relationship.

I wrote back by return post. It was important that he heard from me quickly because I feared that any delay might trigger an impulsive decision to return straight away, when the whole point of our agreement was to allow enough time to provide an opportunity to think seriously about past wrongs, and what we could do to improve matters. On a deeply personal and realistic level, I was beginning to hope that he would decide to stay there. The consequences would undoubtedly prove to be tough on myself with one baby and another on the way, but I felt that it would probably be for the best for all of us in the longer term.

Crucially, at the end of the third week I could see that the money I had left would be running out sooner than I had hoped. I had kept up with paying the weekly rent, the Council rates, and put enough money by for the electricity meter to use, as required, and we also had a good, small stock of food in the cupboard, but I was planning ahead and I could see finances running out after the next couple weeks.

I located the area office for the Department of Health and Social Security. After leaving the pram outside I carried Jimmy in my arms into the offices where I joined a queue. My turn to reach the front of the queue came and I walked up to where a smart young man sat behind a desk. He wore a badge upon which bore his name, Gerald Fairbridge. The civil servant asked for all my basic details first before questioning me about the purpose of my visit.

I explained that my husband had left the family home and gone back to his native Ireland, and that I thought that he wouldn't be returning. He asked for the address in Ireland where he was living, and I gave them his parents' address, saying that I wasn't sure where he would be living but that his parents would know of his whereabouts. I doubted that officials would write to his parents, but even if they did there was no chance on earth that his family would divulge the fact that he was living alongside the rest of them in the tiny two-bedroomed bungalow.

I would be classed as a deserted wife, something that they would have come across many times before, especially in poverty-ridden areas of the city such as ours.

'What were the circumstances of his departure?' Mr Fairbridge asked.

'Well, he had been experiencing difficulties in finding appropriate work, and our relationship had been suffering as a result,' I said.

'What does he do?'

'He is a roofer.' I thought it best not to state general labouring because there must have been scores of jobs available for such work for anyone prepared to work legally. Then I panicked at the thought that there were perhaps equally as many opportunities available for roofers, from which to take his pick!

'Mmm,' Mr Fairbridge commented. 'I *am* surprised.'

'I felt awkward, desperately trying to think of a rejoinder, but you could say that I'd 'peaked'. I couldn't think of one. Fortunately, Mr Fairbridge then added:

'Now, as you probably know, we will be sending out one of our team to see you within the next week or so, to validate and discuss your claim.'

'Of course. I look forward to meeting them. Thank you.'

Gerald proceeded to rubber stamp his handwritten form and popped it in a wire tray on his desk before adding,

'Thank you Mrs Delaney. Good day to you.'

'Good day,' I replied.

In the event that Sean returned home then I would have to cancel my claim for benefit, I thought, but at least I was prepared if he chose not to come back.

I was beginning to feel somewhat restored; rested with my new sleeping patterns; marvelling at Jimmy's development and all that I was learning in relation to my child.

One particular night, I fell asleep immediately after a late feed.

So deep a sleep I'd lapsed into that I hadn't heard the key turning in the lock in the early hours. Since Sean had left I had been in the habit of sliding the two heavy bolts across the back of the door. There came a thudding. I heard a dim cry.

'Sue, it's me. Sean. Let me in.'

I crept, fumbling, downstairs, half asleep, alarmed by this nocturnal jolt.

'It's okay, Sue. Let me in.'

I slid around the bottom stair into the living room and sat, unnerved, on the couch, shaking and shocked at his sudden return, without notice.

In that moment I wanted him to go away, so that I could have some time to think about it all. Common sense told me that he wasn't going to. I couldn't bring myself to open the door. Petrified, I sat, hardly daring to breathe.

His knuckles hit the front window.

'Sue, Sue, open the door. Let me in! It's okay.'

In a whirlpool of emotions I sat gripping the edge of the couch when, without warning, came the almighty smashing of the large, oak front door as it came crashing off its hinges, bolts and all, flying half way up the hall. Sean rushed into the living room. He had actually broken down the whole door with a run up from the kerb and one heave of his shoulder.

'Sue, why didn't you open the door?'

He flung his arms around me and scooped me upright towards him.

I was speechless with shock. The cold night air gusted through the open front doorway as Sean continued with an outpouring of effusive affection about how much he had missed me; he couldn't wait to put his arms around me to tell me how much he loved me, and he asked where his precious son was.

Sean never did anything by halves.

Half an hour later, with the door now wedged upright, hard against the open space, three chairs propped up against it, we drank tea and ate toast. I listened to his colourful stories about Kilkenny, his family, and the life he had been missing before.

The peace of my new life was shattered, and tiny shreds of sadness lay about me.

I couldn't help but wonder whether his unannounced return had been calculated to see if he could catch me out, given his past, paranoid accusations. However, Sean's impetuosity probably gave rise to an instant decision to return and there wouldn't have been time to let me know by mail. That would have required at least four days' preparatory notice and life moved much quicker than that, as far as Sean was concerned.

That afternoon Sean put to me a proposal that he had been hatching since he had set foot on Irish soil: he wanted all three of us to go to live in Kilkenny. He put it to me that, only there did he feel that he could give me, and Jimmy, the life that we deserved, and a good life at that, he assured.

He compared the life we had in Openshaw, living by the dirty main road in a soulless part of Manchester with the simple, healthier life we would have in Kilkenny. He argued that although it was a small city, everyone knew everyone else. It was surrounded by countryside. Life was slower, healthier and simpler.

'Sue, back home people look after each other. You would be loved. Jimmy would be adored by everyone.'

He laughed: 'There's be no shortage of babysitters, that's for sure!'

I wasn't sure why we would need babysitters. I loved caring for my little son and there was no way that I wanted to go gallivanting anywhere at night.

'I'd get work, for certain,' he said persuasively.

'And it'd be daytime work. *Normal* work! We would be surrounded by all of my family and friends. Sue, it's a different life there. Here, you're just left to your own devices with a new baby. No one here gives a damn about anyone: a person could be lying on the floor for weeks and no one would know anything about it, and if they *did* they wouldn't care.'

I so much wanted to be part of a family. The idea of kinship and reciprocity was hugely appealing to me. I knew that he was right about the lack of love and care in our society. His descriptions of life back home, the slower pace, a beautiful environment in which to bring up children, and a loving family sounded so much richer than what we had in this squalid house on the fringes of Manchester.

But what of him? Could this leopard change its spots?

For one thing, I reflected, he would have his family scrutinising his every move. That might rein him in a bit. Then there's the Catholic Church which, from what Sean told me, played a major role in regulating behaviours.

Apparently the Priest visited regularly. Sean had long ago told me that when the familiar-sounding knock on the door came it would spur the whole family into action: the television was lifted at speed into the nearest bedroom, and any incriminating evidence of an unGodly existence, such an empty beer bottle or an ash tray was promptly whisked out of sight, at the speed of lightening, before welcoming the venerated Father indoors.

Over the next few days I became enticingly drawn towards the idea of relocation. I started to think about the implications of such a move. What would I stand to lose in trying? If he was right and our lives became so much more improved then it might actually turn out to be the best move I would ever make, for me and the children, *and* perhaps even our marriage.

Such a move, however, would be a mammoth undertaking for me, and for Jimmy too, and especially with a new baby on the way to add complications. I realised that it was an enormous gamble. It wasn't something I could do lightly.

I mulled over whether I should merely continue to tread the same path, but with *two* children in this bleak city heartland, with a husband who didn't fit well into this alienating landscape, and whose actions threatened to have a continued negative impact on me and the children? Alternatively should I try to privately pursue some sort of assistance in somehow extricating myself from him? In order to try to leave him I would need help to achieve it, *and* to keep him at bay. I couldn't begin to imagine how I could do that. Or lastly, should I try to make a go of his idea, and then at least if that didn't work out it might be easier for me to walk away with my babies, to try to start all over again?

At nineteen, through necessity, I had learned the art of making difficult decisions by examining different pros and cons, including those of worst case scenario outcomes. The case for staying put, if we remained together, seemed inexorably to hold bleak expectations. But if I were to give such a proposed move my very best endeavours and it *still* didn't work then one day, at least, I would be able to tell both my children that I had been prepared to go to great lengths to save the marriage in order for them to have the family life that I wanted for them. That I was more than willing to risk so much, at great personal cost, to give them what was regarded as a 'normal,' family upbringing.

In mid twentieth century Britain a cohesive, nuclear family was vigorously upheld as the proper means by which to bring up healthy children. Conversely, a 'broken family', as it was then termed, was a recipe for malady and dysfunction, we were told.

Crucially, also, I knew and understood the importance, particularly for my son, of children having a father figure, and I did not want them to grow up thinking that any decision I made now denied them an opportunity to have a full and normal upbringing.

I finally decided that I would try my very best, putting every last shred of effort possible into making this marriage work, despite our differences, and go to live in Sean's country of birth, as he wished. For if, then, things failed completely I could live with a clear conscience, and hope that my children would one day forgive me for what was then regarded as a 'relegation' to a single parent household, and any subsequent stigmatization, and other problems, that would undoubtedly arise during their growing years.

Sean couldn't have been more thrilled with my acceptance of his suggestion. He expressed unmitigated pride at the thought of being able to take his new wife, and baby boy, with another new baby on the way also, back to his home town. He wanted all of his friends and family to get to know me and he seemed to be in no doubt at all that I would love living in Kilkenny.

He wrote to his parents to tell them the news, and about our latest good fortune: that we were expecting our second child. He expressed the news as if it were a 'feather in his cap', when all he had done was help himself to what he regarded were his conjugal rights.

We packed up the little that we owned and on the day before we emigrated I arranged for us to go to visit Mum and Dad. It was an awkward meeting, and I found myself, as many women do, filling in the gaps of silence with chit chat to make the whole thing more bearable. Dad did his best, asking Sean what line of work he would be able to undertake. Mum scurried around with tea and biscuits, and she put on a good face and wished us well in our new life. As we said our goodbyes, I turned away with sadness. Mum's life had been, and still was, a difficult one, and she probably feared that mine too would result in similar subjugation. We were very different women, though, and I viewed this new venture as an open-ended experience, and not the beginning and end of a story. Unlike Mum I had a fire in my belly. I was determined to get the very best for my children, and for my life too. I hoped that it would be in Ireland, but I knew even then that nothing is carved in stone.

CHAPTER 13

Before emigrating to Ireland, of all the potential costs and benefits I had meticulously conjectured I could never have foreseen the love affair that began on that spring day in nineteen sixty nine. My love of the island transcends the events which ensued, and has done ever since.

From the first moment of our arrival in the city of Kilkenny, its sights and sounds couldn't have captivated me more. I drank in a sense of a world which refused to catch up. Time stood still. Though we were more than half way through the twentieth century Kilkenny heeded none of it. Shop windows were bedecked in spartan fashion, frequently with only one or two items of wares taking centre stage. A baker's shop had three loaves indiscriminately balanced on a breadboard as its focal point in the window. A tobacconist's had at its showcase a velvet curtain backcloth with a small, velvet covered dais upon which sat, simply and unapologetically, a packet of cigarettes and a pipe. There was a distinct sense of snub to commercialisation, as if to say 'we do it our way' and, 'besides, the commercial activity speaks for itself'.

On the cobbled road leading from the railway station, up John's Street and over the old bridge there were still hooves clattering over it, pulling milk churns and, sometimes, nothing. Nuns walked by, two-by-two, their great wimples pointing heavenward like a scene out of the middle ages. Locals stopped to pass the time of day, resting their wicker baskets on the ground, while they discussed the latest gossip or the drunken brawl that had spilled out of McCready's bar at midnight.

We walked up Barracks Road, past the handball courts where Sean had honed his skills. Turning left into Fintan Street, lined with what I regarded as a row of bungalows, there, half way down, Sean's family all crammed into the tiny house he called home.

No sooner had the gate banged shut but the front door opened and the entire Delaney family tumbled out; mother Mary, father Brendan and a host of children, in addition to his elder brother Fergus, and his Scottish wife, Erin.

I smiled at this gaggle of a welcoming party, such was their excitement at our homecoming.

'Hello! It's so nice to be here, and to finally meet you all,' I said, trying to take in all that was happening, and wanting to appear to be friendly.

Sean introduced his younger siblings:

'This is Kitty. This is Mona. This is Mikey. This is...........'

'Come on inside,' Mary interrupted. 'There's a pot of tea just brewed by the hearth, and I'm sure that you want to rest after your long journey.'

We were ushered in, as all eyes were on me and baby Jimmy.

'Oh God, love him,' Mary cried, 'will you look at this infant, Brendan, sure he's the spit of Sean.'

I was far too polite to say so, but I had thought that Jimmy's features resembled mine, and not his father's, but who was I to argue as the Prodigal Son not only returneth but was already basking in his siblings' popularity and now handing out chocolate bars, as if Ireland had seen none of them before.

This happy homecoming belonged to a different world of simplicity and innocence. They would have no knowledge of corruption, of sexual deviance, or their brother's underground activities, and the great religious scandals within the church had yet to be unearthed.

The house was tiny. There was no bathroom, and the installation of a toilet had been a late addition, built in the garden, two steps from the back door. To wash, we had to boil a kettle on the stove and bring a basin into the room that had been set aside as our bedroom. That, at least, I had to be thankful for; a separate space in which to sleep, unlike most of the family who shared beds, top to tail, and had no privacy in which to wash, dress or make love.

Sean's older brother, Fergus, had recently returned home from working in Glasgow, bringing his new bride, Erin, and their baby, Oscar. Erin was expecting their second child. She was Roman Catholic, and therefore I was the only non-Catholic in the house, and I felt that it distinguished me as the outsider. I was someone whose baptism somehow symbolized a liaison with the devil. Our different religious backgrounds were of no importance to me, but to an unenlightened Roman Catholic household such as this, it set me apart.

This was intended to be our home, for at least a matter of a few weeks until Sean could find somewhere for us to live. Or that's how I understood it to be.

Erin had lived here for a few months and had already become assimilated into the fabric of the tiny house. She went to mass with the rest of the family every Sunday, always wearing her black veil over her head, and looking every inch the modest person she really was. She seemed to be undaunted by the cramped conditions and the age-old ritual of having to carry a small bowl of water into her tiny space to perform daily ablutions.

On the evening of our arrival, there could be no settling in, nor chance of an early night's sleep which one might have expected, given our long journey. The family were insistent that occasions like this one should be celebrated and marked with a drink or two at the local bar, Docherty's. I was assured that Jimmy would be well looked after.

I fed my darling baby and made sure that he was sound asleep. The last thing I wanted to do was to go out, but I felt a pressure to try to fit in with the traditions of Sean's family. Thus, I found myself, as if in a film noir, sitting on a hard bench in Docherty's noisy, smoke-filled bar with the craic flowing around my head, as I tried hard to keep my eyes open. Drinks lined up from nowhere, as I quietly insisted that I couldn't drink alcohol. The queue of whiskies became a line of orange juices. I didn't know how I was going to swallow so much citrus in one evening.

Glasses were raised to me, to both of us, to Jimmy, to our unborn baby; fiddles were played and songs were sung. It became a blur like no other. As we all piled out after closing time one of our number decided that we should go and buy some fish and chips for our supper, and for those of the young resident babysitters.

Erin and our in-laws strolled on home ahead of us while Sean and Fergus queued in front of me at the Fish Bar on Barracks Road. As I waited I became aware of an inebriated admirer, a young man who waited behind me in the queue. Out of the corner of my eye I detected more than a kindly glance as he sized me up and down lasciviously.

Suddenly stricken by panic, and never having given him so much as a whiff of a 'glad eye', I fixed my gaze rigidly ahead at the counter where salt and vinegar were flying in all directions. Alas, it was too late! All I heard was Sean's expletive-filled shriek:

'What the fuck do you think *you're* looking at!' as he clocked the offending lecherous admirer whose drunken eyes rolled over my form.

In a great flash of fury, obscenities and testosterone, Sean flew across the waiting crowd and dragged the man outside, pummelling him to the ground. Other men rushed out and jumped on top of Sean to try to stem the punches and mitigate the damage, dragging him off the unfortunate man, whilst two male passers-by hauled the unfortunate customer upright. Gone now was the lustful, drooling countenance, but replaced with bloodstains and shiners that could light up his path home.

Rectitude and composure fully restored, we reached Fintan Street, with bags of chips and a few battered fish to divvy up between us all.

In bed, exhausted, and having experienced a unique inauguration to the Delaney household, the images of the evening rattled through my head like the stills of a Charlie Chaplin film.

More celebrations at Docherty's followed the first: late night fish and chip suppers with the children and adults gathered around the table in the living room, followed by songs, as each child sang a favourite Irish ballad, and a number of the adults too. There was disappointment all round that I couldn't contribute a solo performance of my own. Had I known about this tradition I might have taken the trouble beforehand to learn all the words of one song by heart, but it also transpired that I was little prepared for everything else that followed; all the dress rehearsals in the world couldn't have carried me effortlessly through this drama.

When it became clear that I simply couldn't sustain repeated evenings out at Docherty's bar the men in the household continued theirs.

One evening, waiting for Sean to return, my patience with these night time binging sessions was beginning to wear thin. I managed to contain my disapproval until, that is, he reached out towards me in bed, wanting an intimate night-cap that would top off nicely his evening's recreation. That did it! I snapped! My raging, post-natal *and* now, *pre*-natal hormones, formed an unholy liaison that gave rise to me letting rip.

'Don't you dare!' I growled, in a low key so as not to wake up the whole house. 'You didn't tell me that you would be going out every night, drinking yourself *stupid!* I don't want any of this. As for expecting anything of me now, you can forget about it! I am not your comforter, or party piece to be savoured at the end of your revelries. Go to hell!'

'Sshhhhh,' he chided. 'They'll all hear!'

'Well, let them,' I said. 'All this might be normal and acceptable for them but it certainly isn't for me!'

The next morning, when I got up to prepare Jimmy's breakfast, there lay an uneasy stillness throughout the house. Some of the children hadn't appeared, as they usually did. Brendan, who normally made Mary an early morning cup of tea and took his outside, after which he would have a wash and shave in the open air, was nowhere to be seen.

All of a sudden, as if waiting for my arrival at the kitchen sink it was as if an orchestra struck up into an angry prelude, fast and furious, as his mother Mary's voice burst into loud, stormy resonance.

'If *she* thinks she can behave like that in my house, with *my* son, and after the welcome she's had, then she can just fuck off and get out of my house!'

I felt dumbstruck; welded to the spot; horrified by this woman's outburst. It had been premeditated for my ears, and the rest of the family was to hear it too. I was shocked at the response to what had only been a few heated words and she couldn't possibly have known or understood anything about it, or been able to consider whether perhaps my annoyance might have been justified. Or was it the case that, in her world, where women conceived one child after another throughout their marriages there was no justification to object to a husband's demands; maybe it was deemed to be his *right*? Or was it more to do with God's will?

I grabbed the foods in haste and quickly gathered up my things, then lifted Jimmy into my arms also.

'Where are you going?' Sean abruptly sat up in bed. 'Sue, whatever she said, she doesn't mean it. They're just not used to a woman in the house having a voice, that's all. Take Erin, she's as quiet as a church mouse.'

'Yes, well now I know why Erin is so highly rated. She's Catholic, quiet and submissive. She fits in well,' I said, making for the door.

'I'm sorry, Sean, but your mum has made it more than clear that she wants me to go. How could I possibly stay here after that?'

I closed the front door of the house and wandered down the street, not knowing where I was going. Something had changed in me. I had summoned my courage. I wasn't isolated any more. I was surrounded by people. People who needed to hear me, whether they agreed with me or not.

I found a spot in the field behind the house and sat down in a grassy glade with my precious son. I fed him some formula, and he lapped up the cold contents of a jar of spinach and potato puree, and beamed back at me, his two new bottom teeth gleaming at me from his darling mouth. I laid him down and removed his soiled nappy, creamed him, and after putting him into a fresh white nappy I sat him down amongst the buttercups and grasses.

A familiar voice rang out from the end of the field. Sean had come looking for me. My new-found courage knew no bounds now: I handed him the dirty nappy.

'Perhaps you could take that back; sluice it, soak it, then give it a wash. And we'll need somewhere to sleep tonight. If you don't manage to come up with anywhere I'm going to have to look for the local Garda's barracks. Maybe they can help me.'

'Look Sue, mammy didn't mean it,' he reiterated.

'Has she said that?'

'No, not exactly, but I know she doesn't want you out here.' He sat down with us in the long grass.

'I didn't choose to be out here, but your mother has made it crystal clear. She doesn't want me to stay in her house. We'll need to rent a room as from tonight.'

Sean went quiet.

'To be honest, I think you might be right, after all. I'm going to see what I can find,' he said, jumping to his feet. 'I'll be back.'

Quite how Sean achieved it I'll never know, but in the late afternoon, after I had wandered around nearby streets, carrying a heavy bag full of baby supplies of every kind, he caught up with me to tell me of his coup.

'I've got us a place! It's in John's Street over the Pharmacy. Come on, let's go!'

I had to give it to him. He had managed to achieve what I secretly thought might have been impossible.

'How did you find it?' I asked, as we walked the long way round the town, in order to avoid passing the house wherein many sets of eyes would observe our movements.

'Well, sure, I was in Docherty's at lunchtime and I put the word out that I was looking for a place, and did anyone know of anything going. Didn't Eamon Murphy pipe up that Malachy Dooley was the man to contact? Our man has property coming out of his ears, and he might just have something, says Eamon.'

'So you contacted Mr Dooley?'

'I found his name in the phone book. He's some big noise around here, and he told me that, as it happens, he had something that became vacant only this week. Jesus, he wreaks of money, in his breeches, and all. He showed me round, I paid a month's rent, and we shook hands on it. It's ours, Sue. You'll love it.'

By the time we arrived in John's Street all of the shops had closed for the day, and it was fairly quiet. The door that stood next to the Pharmacy took us into a long hallway and up two flights of stairs to a small apartment which overlooked the street. We came to learn that Malachy Dooley owned the whole building, including the Pharmacy on the ground floor.

We had a small kitchen, a living-cum-bedroom and a tiny bathroom. It was enough for us, and I was grateful for the privacy, and for indoor plumbing.

I knew that the money that Sean had brought with him, from his activities in Glossop, had to run out sometime soon; so we sat down that evening to have a serious discussion about work, what was available to him, and how he was going to embark on a new job search.

'Don't worry, Sue, I'll get work alright. I just have to put the word out.'

I knew what that meant. More lunchtime drinking sessions at Docherty's, followed by a game or two in the handball court!

Sean found some work on a building site in Thomastown, nearby, and this signalled the start of a more settled period for us. He was picked up by 'the lads' and transported every weekday, there and back. At weekends he was keen to show me the beautiful city in which we lived.

He took me around the town centre, past the churches that he knew, the abbeys, the cathedral, and the fateful school where 'the brothers' had beaten him regularly. He showed me the handball court. He was proud of his place of birth.

On our first Saturday since moving to John's Street we stopped to sit outside a small cafe at the other end of town and he ordered two glasses of fizzy lemonade, each with a scoop of ice cream floating on top of it. If only life could be as sweet as in this moment, I thought, as Sean wiped the ice cream that was running down Jimmy's chin and watched our darling baby sink his open mouth into the vanilla cone.

Each day I pushed Jimmy out in a pram that we had acquired second-hand in the local market. I was keen to get to know Kilkenny, which seemed so unlike the large, sprawling, dirty towns with which I was more familiar. There was the beautiful castle, a spectacular relic of the middle ages, with its lush grounds surrounded by the River Nore, all of which I could see from our back yard in John Street and where I hung out the washing to dry. Who else pegs out their washing, I marvelled daily, looking at such a majestic sight, and listening to the sounds of the river rushing by?

I regularly walked down the main thoroughfare of the High Street, peering into the shops and reading the plaques outside the historic buildings to find out what was going on inside, and upstairs in their chambers. I wandered down side streets, soaking up the history, the many convents and the religious landmarks with holy fountains outside, where passers-by dipped their fingers and marked their heads and chests with the sign of the cross in deference to their maker.

Priests were a regular sight in the town as they made their way about their business. Friars and monks also, with their hooded cloaks and habits, along with nuns, added to the spectacle of a city whose present was still inextricably interwoven with religious life and history.

There were many staring faces, locals eyeing up the new girl. I was the *English girl*. I knew that I somehow looked different. I also looked like a Protestant.

Their eyes would follow me as I walked past, and I imagined the gossip:

'Would you look at her! *She's* the *English girl*. She married one of the Delaney's, don't you know. One baby, and another on the way. They say that he's always hanging around Docherty's *and* the handball courts up Barracks Road. Poor child.'

In the local greengrocer's in John Street, and the bakery across the road from our flat, when I entered each it seemed like I was the cause of immediate distraction. Conversations about how many potato farls or blaa buns would pause as they looked round to see the new girl. I would tentatively smile and say a quiet hello, as they nodded and resumed their transactions.

Irish breads have a long tradition which stems from the time of the potato famine, and I found the sheer variety of shapes, textures and tastes tantalising, and a sight to behold. I thought that they put our bloomers and split tins to shame, not to mention the bland sliced loaves wrapped in waxed paper that filled our shops back home.

Sadly, it didn't take long before our 'happy family bubble' burst. It seemed to coincide with the abrupt curtailment of Sean's work.

'Ah Jesus, Sue, I have some bad news for us,' he said when he arrived home one evening. 'When we lined up this afternoon to receive our dues Seamus O'Reilly announced that they were laying off all the lads, as of today.'

'No!' I cried, in disbelief. 'I thought it was all going well. What happened?'

'Well, apparently, the firm has hit some legal problems, some sort of problem with the land registry, or something; anyway, it's to do with a small matter that wasn't approved before they started. Seamus said it's just a tiny detail, a hiccup, and he's going to be in touch the minute it's all resolved.'

'Well how long is that likely to take, I wonder?'

Sean shrugged his shoulders and raised the palm of his hands, then slapped them down by his sides, looking glum and introspective.

Trying to lift matters, he added: 'Don't worry, Sue, tomorrow I'll get myself out there and look for something else to fill the gap in the meantime.'

Paid work for him became intermittent, and short term; a couple of days here or there, and then, nothing. It didn't stop him going out each day, playing handball and having a drink or two. Sometimes, if quite a number of the men gathered to watch the game someone would open up a bet and Sean would come home with a pittance he had earned.

After two weeks tensions were mounting between us because there was very little money coming in. When Malachy Dooley called to collect his rent, the landlord became impatient with me because it wasn't being paid on time. I would tell Sean what promises I had been forced to make to him, agreeing to his short extensions, just to keep him away from the door. Sometimes I would tell Malachy that the money was 'on its way', when I had no idea where Sean was, or how to get in touch with him.

With greater hardships the balance of power between us was shifting. I was beginning to raise the difficulties I was experiencing with Sean and express frustration in a way that I wouldn't have dared to in Manchester.

'Look Sue, I'm trying my fucking best. What else can I do?'

'But surely there must be *some* jobs which are available that you could get? The fact of the matter is, we don't have enough money coming in to pay the rent, and to feed us, Sean. The new baby is due very soon and Jimmy isn't a year old yet, and so I can't go out to work at the moment. We're going to have to apply to try to get some support of some kind.'

'For Christ's sake, Sue, will ye keep your voice down. We can't have *them* hearing downstairs. They'll call the Garda at the drop of a hat, and it'll be me they take down to the barracks. I told ye, the Guarda here are renowned for beating up people like me.'

I wanted to have a rational discussion about our increasingly fraught financial circumstances, and to explore possible strategies, but each time I mentioned the issue Sean seemed unable or unwilling to engage with me. His way of dealing with it was to walk out.

Since I was the one left to face the landlord, and I too who managed the shopping and household meals, I was becoming increasingly worried about the situation. Arguments would ensue and Sean would frequently disappear for a week, sometimes more. Periodically, I would find money pushed under the door. I had no idea where he managed to get it from, but I suspected that it was probably borrowed, direct from under his parents' mattress. No bank accounts for them. Whatever, the money went straight to Malachy Dooley in order to keep the roof over our heads.

When things were bad between us Sean would simply stay away. At his parents' house there would be no questions asked. I never knew, from one week to the next, when to expect him home. As a result, I spent much of the time on my own with our little boy, who was now almost walking. Meanwhile, our unborn baby was scoring more points than ever for the famous 'Kilkenny Cats' hurling team.

CHAPTER 14

Sean acquired a temporary job working on a farm not far from the outskirts of the city. For a few weeks he came home and family life resumed for us, almost as if there had been no interruptions.

On one particular Saturday afternoon I was preparing our evening meal when my waters suddenly broke, and within seconds the kitchen floor became awash with my baby's protective fluids. Taken completely by surprise, I waddled to the bathroom, drenched, as my attention was diverted to my second baby's imminent arrival.

The next morning, a beautiful, sunny September day in 1969, I was woken early by nagging discomfort in my lower abdomen. I alerted Sean to my contractions, and staggered to the bathroom. This time I didn't need an enema; my body reacted naturally to the anxiety that I felt; I was more aware, this time, of what the job of giving birth entailed.

Sean swung into action.

'I'm going to get Mammy,' he cried. Anywhere else he might have thought fit to run down to the local phone box first to call for emergency help, but not here in Ireland. Mothers knew best all about childbirth, in this land where it was every woman's profession.

He returned, accompanied by his mother, Mary. I was lying on the bed, gripped by recurring contractions.

'Go and phone St Luke's,' she instructed Sean. With that, he headed off again to the nearest telephone box at the top of John's Street to contact the hospital. She turned her attention to me.

'Get up, Sue. Get up, now,' she urged, and she helped me off the bed to stand upright. 'You have to walk around. It'll help you get there quicker.' She put her arm around my waist and began marching me around the flat. My instinct was to want to lie down, to try to rest in between contractions. I learned many years later that Mary was indeed right, but the sheer effort of walking whilst gripped with pain was arduous, to say the least when, in fact, I wanted to double over and rock my pain away.

Sean returned, looking agitated. This time, there was no elation; no excited, happy countenance, as he stood by looking helpless, as women's business took over. I was so preoccupied by the contractions and the thoughts of what was to follow that I wasn't aware of something else which, with the benefit of hindsight, was patently troubling him.

A bell rang downstairs. Sean leapt into action again, probably glad to be of use somehow, and returned with two tall nuns who were dressed from head-to-toe in white; white habits, white veils, and wearing long white starched aprons, signifying the need for protection from women's business. I hadn't expected the church to be involved in childbirth, but this was a country steeped in religious intervention in most aspects of life and I was simply glad of any help in this, my second labour.

The two nuns, both stony-faced, asked Mary to step aside as they took charge and began to lead me down the steep staircase. They helped me climb into the waiting ambulance, and I was glad to succumb to the stretcher inside. I became aware of one of the nuns telling Sean that he couldn't come with me, and would have to telephone for news later on. He and his mother stood by the back doors of the ambulance, with Mary holding Jimmy in her arms, and Sean saying that he would see me soon.

'Remember, Sue, I love you.'

Mary also shouted in to me:

'Now don't you worry about this little man. He'll be taken good care of, for sure.'

I put up my hand to acknowledge both, as one of the nuns shut the doors firmly, with the three of us on board in the back.

The women in white sat down. Not a word passed between us as the vehicle drove speedily over the cobbled streets, making its bumpy way to the hospital at the other end of the city. When we arrived, the nuns asked me to get up and climb out of the ambulance, and I was escorted by one of them as the other went to look for a wheelchair. They summoned a porter to take me to the maternity department, at which point the nuns took their leave of us.

In the maternity wing I was wheeled into a small room, where the same nuns reappeared. One of them asked me to get on to the table and, no sooner had I lay down, but both promptly left the room. I had felt intimidated by their presence, and communication was in short supply. I didn't want to appear to be a troublesome or demanding patient. After all, I was a 'foreigner'. Furthermore, at this critical time, I felt especially vulnerable and in need of care to support me through the process of childbirth. Already I had observed that the nuns seemed to exert extraordinary authority in their healthcare capacity. Further, I noted Sean's and Mary's deference to the nuns, and also how the porter scrambled to attention as the nuns approached.

Looking round I couldn't help comparing the room with that of the delivery room in St Mary's in Manchester where I had given birth to Jimmy twelve months earlier.

This room was stark, and contained only a sink and some cupboards, and there was no equipment, or staff. I kept wondering when I would see the midwife, but none appeared. I decided to try to remain as calm as I could when the contractions occurred, inhaling and exhaling with forbearance, and consciously trying to keep calm.

Fifteen minutes passed and still no-one appeared. After another ten minutes or so a male doctor, whom I presumed to be a gynaecologist, poked his head around the door briefly and looked over at me, then disappeared. And still, no one had examined my cervix to assess dilations or how far along I was in my labour.

After about forty minutes the same nuns entered the room, and they positioned themselves at either side of the bed. Neither had given me their name. The contractions had become excruciatingly painful and I looked towards the nun on my right hand side.

'Sister, could I please have some gas and air?'

'Her eyes bore down on me and, answering tersely, and almost in ridicule:

'There's no gas and air in here, girl!'

I was beginning to learn what little help was given to birthing mothers, and how much less advanced was Ireland's maternity care provision, than in the UK. No-one had examined me, and the nuns were there only to make sure that I delivered a live baby, and to cut the umbilical cord. However, I still had a way to go, and the most painful part had yet to come.

Flanking me on either side of the bed one nun instructed: 'Now cross your arms over your chest, like this.' The same nun who had ridiculed me for asking for help with the pain crossed one of her arms over the other.

She continued: 'And grab hold of our hands, and pull on them when the pain comes.'

This was new to me. In the library books I had scoured at home none of the modern texts had described this as a possible scenario, but I did as I was told, and pulled each time I had a painful contraction. I imagined tugging them both so hard that their heads butted somewhere in mid-air, but they balanced their respective weights, legs outstretched under their voluminous habits, and pulled backwards.

I was pushing with all my might, but the baby wouldn't come. The pain was horrendous. I wanted to ask if there was someone who might be able to assess whether a cut might be necessary in widening the birth canal, as had happened the previous year, but I didn't have the courage.

At one point, during a painful contraction, exhausted from pushing, I let out a groan so loud, that the same nun who mocked my request for pain relief, sharply rebuked me for daring to let a shriek escape.

'*What* are you yelling for, girl, there's no need for that. *Just push hard!*' Sage advice from a celibate, and one who would never experience labour pains, smear tests, prolapse or hysteroscopy!

I didn't know how much harder I could push. I felt as if my uterus was going to explode. Distressed, and drenched in sweat, the need to keep pushing seemed relentless and then, suddenly, as I pushed hard again I felt my flesh suddenly rip apart as my baby's head forced its way through. This was followed by the need for another hard push, and I finally delivered the rest of its body.

I lay shaking, feeling traumatised, glad it was all over. I fell back in a state of grateful collapse. One of the nuns cut the umbilical cord and the other swooped up the baby, hung its long body upside down and gave a sharp slap to its back.

'You have yourself a daughter. Here you are.' She handed me my baby girl. I quietly wept with the strain and emotion of it all, as I blinked down at my lovely little Irish newborn.

Tears spilling over my cheeks, I chuckled at her beautiful little face. She had a full head of thick, brown, unruly hair, and big dark eyes to match, and the most beautiful face I could only ever have imagined. She looked like her father. She had a big curl in the middle of her forehead, just like the one I had seen coiffed on the forehead of the flamboyant hairdresser I had seen on television, Mr Teasy Weasy! He couldn't have styled it better himself!

I hadn't realised it then, but my flesh had torn in exactly the same place that I had been cut twelve months' earlier in order to make way for my son's passage into the world. And so, I *had* required intervention, after all, and since no help was given *this* time, the pressure of this larger baby had resulted in an injury that was neither stitched afterwards, nor healed in a way that the deft stitchsmith in Manchester would have approved.

Minutes later, my daughter was whisked from my arms. I was asked to climb down from the labour table. Shakily, I managed to find enough residual stamina to haul myself up and into the waiting wheelchair without keeling over. My eyes fell shut and I lurched between sleep and wakefulness as I was pushed through doors, and along a corridor. No nurses; no midwife; no pain relief; and no stitching of a tear. Thank goodness it was all over, I lamented. I could only hope that my baby hadn't suffered too much stress in wanting to emerge sooner than had finally occurred.

I vaguely remember clambering out of the wheelchair and up into a bed on a ward.

'Now then, there's a little food left over from dinner: would you like a pork sausage or two and some mashed potato?' A nurse wearing a starched blue cap peered over me and woke me to make a peace offering. I couldn't face it, but I agreed to having some jelly. The problem arose that, in my fatigue, I seemed to have lost my ability to co-ordinate my eyes and hand as the defiant dessert hit my cheek and slid off the spoon; down my face, continuing its descent inside my nightdress and piling up on my matronly bosom like some great melting glacier. This necessitated more fumblings and repeated scoops at the elusive mound before finally managing to hone it back up and into my waiting mouth.

I wondered about my baby's whereabouts. I was informed by a nurse that all of the babies were placed in a nursery along the corridor from the ward. I also wondered where Sean was. I tried to stay awake, convinced that he would be visiting very soon. It was Sunday after all, and it wasn't as if he went to mass. My eyelids drooped continuously and I kept drifting in and out of sleep. I woke again and glanced at my watch: two hours after giving birth there was still no sign of him. Other proud husbands came to see their wives during the afternoon visiting period, but there was no sign of Sean. Nobody came.

I asked the senior nurse on the ward if he had telephoned.

'Not that I'm aware of, Mrs Delaney, but you must get some rest now. I'm sure he'll be up later to see both yourself and baby.'

I wanted him to be as happy as I was about our beautiful daughter. Just as with our firstborn I wanted him to want to see her; I had done all the hard work in delivering her, and the very least he could do was to show up and see how we both were. I wasn't seeking an accolade. It was, after all, about seven hours since I'd left him standing in John's Street.

More hours passed as I lapsed drowsily in and out of sleep. I could hear the thundering aluminium trolley delivering the evening meal, jolting and rattling its way up the main corridor.

This time I managed to eat a little; my hand managed to hit the jackpot as I spooned small quantities of shepherd's pie into my mouth, followed by a slice of pear and ice cream. After the catering staff had cleared away most of the tea time dishes from the ward, and the 'coast was clear', I decided to take action.

I could wait no longer to see my baby. I got out of bed and crept slowly down the corridor, sore and aching, and with only a sanitary towel to prevent drips of blood hitting the floor. Slithering along at a snail's pace I passed a room from where a woman's voice shouted out and groaned.

'Jesus Christ, please help me. Please God, help me.' Staff walked by with plates and jugs as if that poor woman couldn't be heard. I wondered if the nuns were eating *their* meal, or perhaps at prayer, thanking their own celestial husband for his goodness, instead of watching over all those wretched women who were left alone for long periods of their labour without pain relief. The woman making the noise couldn't have been at the stage of crossing her arms and pulling at nuns' hands or, like me, she would no doubt have been told to shut up and get on with it.

Further along the corridor I reached a large glass window, behind which many cots were lined up in rows. I pushed open the door, and a nurse who was feeding a baby asked:

'Can I help you?'

'Thank you nurse. I gave birth earlier on and I just wanted to see my baby, if you don't mind?'

'Not at all. What is your name?'

'Susan Delaney, 'I replied.

'Aah, she's over here. I tell you, this girl has a fine pair of lungs on her.'

I walked between the rows of tiny bodies to see my darling baby. I would recognise that curl anywhere.

'I'd like to hold her for a few minutes, nurse, would that be okay?'

'I'm not supposed to…….., but, just for a few minutes, now.'

I lifted my daughter into my arms and whispered to her, planting a kiss on her face, and taking in breaths of her sweet skin. I hoped that she sensed that I was her mama. I was fine now.

'I'll take good care of her, and I'll bring her through to ye ready for visiting time. Go and rest, now.'

'Thank you, nurse,' I said, as I made my way back to my bed on the ward. As I passed the labour room the same woman was still crying out with pain.

'Holy Mother, Mother o' God, please help me!' And the food trolley rattled along back to the kitchens.

I was beginning to feel a mounting grievance towards Sean. I reflected upon the state of our marriage and about Sean's regular absences from our lives; the struggle that comprised my day-to-day life, with constant worry about how to pay the rent, and where the next amount of money might come from to feed us. His absence now, from what should have been one of the most important days in his life, and most certainly mine, distressed me. It marked a watershed in my thinking.

The start of the evening visiting hour arrived. At seven o' clock some husbands poured in with their flowers and gifts and I sat, propped up, watching them. I smiled at my darling daughter who was now sleeping soundly in a cot next to me. At least I had her next to me for a few hours. I could marvel at her perfection, and I began also to worry about my baby boy. I knew how much he would be missing his mama, and I hoped that he was being happily distracted and cared for in Fintan Street.

Half an hour into the visiting period, Sean walked unsteadily into the ward, followed by Mary. Both looked uneasy, uncertain of how they would find me. I couldn't manage a smile. I wasn't happy with Sean, and he knew it. He bent down to kiss my cheek, and the smell of alcohol hit me. I turned towards him. His eyes confirmed that he had been drinking heavily.

'Where have you been all day? It's Sunday. Why didn't you come earlier, and why are you drunk?'

'Sue, I couldn't tell you this morning, with all that was going on. But I had an inter-county match today in Carlow. I won it, and I was presented with a fine cup. The lads bought me a few drinks, and I came as soon as I could.'

I stared straight ahead and said nothing. There was silence as he walked around the other side of the bed to look at his daughter.

'She's a fine girl, Sue. Mammy, will you look at her! And look at that curl. God love her.'

Mary walked round to see her granddaughter.

'Jesus, Sue, she's a beautiful baby. What did she weigh?'

'Seven pounds and fourteen ounces. By the way, thank you, Mary, for your help this morning,' I added.

'Sure, it was nothing. And Jimmy is as happy a little boy as ye ever did see,' she said. 'We've told him that he has a new baby brother or sister.'

My darling son wouldn't, of course, have understood, but her sentiment was well-intentioned. I watched Sean's face as his eyes tried to focus, and his eyelids repeatedly lapsed downwards in the way I had seen many times before. He must have had a skinful of Guinness; enough to oil the whole bus that carried the Kilkenny handball revellers back from Carlow.

He studied my sullen stare for a moment, and then, quite unexpectedly said: 'You're going to leave me, aren't you, Sue?'

With knee jerk alacrity I fired back: 'You're dead right, I am,' little realising the speed at which he would convey this live pearl of wisdom to his mother.

'Do you hear that, Mammy?' he said.

Until then Mary had been standing back from us, behind her son, in what I felt was probably, in part, respect for the interaction between a man and his wife on such an occasion. But perhaps also because she had probably worked hard to drag her son along to perform his husbandly duties in the midst of great handball jubilation and celebration, and needed now to gather her strength. She might even have gone into Docherty's, to haul him out and, as was probably prudent on these drink-induced occasions, didn't want to stand in the way of any acrimonious crossfire.

She leant forward.

'What's that?' she enquired, feigning interest in our stilted discourse.

'She says she's going to leave me,' he said, as he swivelled round and almost lost his balance in his bid to include her in the exchange. Interestingly, he had selectively omitted to tell her that *he* had initiated the subject.

'Oh, Sue. You don't mean that, say you don't.'

I couldn't answer that one, and I returned my gaze directly ahead of me, in something of a defiant 'I refuse to comment further' moment.

I was the only one of the new mothers with a drunken husband. Had he been drunk as a result of the birth of his daughter, that might have counted for something. But the truth was that his success in the game of handball, and the male-centric social milieu meant far more to him that *I* did, or our family, even on a day as precious to me as this one.

Eight o' clock arrived, and a couple of the fathers in the ward took their leave. Sean stood up, swaying unsteadily and uttering his farewell, saying that he would visit me again soon. I looked up at him dejectedly, feeling let down with his protracted absence during today, of all days.

When he had gone, I glanced around the ward at the other mothers with their bunches of flowers, magazines and bags of treats on their bed side table. Not for a minute had I expected Sean to come bearing gifts. Presents didn't figure in my world. I would have been happy just to see him earlier, or to have learned that he had telephoned the ward and sent his love to us both. Still, I would enjoy looking at everyone else's flowers.

On reflection, I felt that in all likelihood my post-natal fatigue and hormonal imbalance had made me react badly to Sean's bait. I realised that his big Sunday match was probably what had been preying on his mind earlier in the day; something which, nonetheless, he hadn't shared with me on previous days when he would have already known of its scheduling.

The next day I was visited on the ward by the Priest of St Luke's hospital, Father O'Connor. He sat down beside the bed and asked how I was, and also how my baby was getting on. I thought it very kind of him to visit me and I responded by telling him of my happiness at the birth of a baby girl; that I felt blessed, having had a son and, now, a daughter also.

I soon learned, however, of the real reason behind his visit. He asked me what we were intending to call our child. I said that we had discussed the name, Katy, and that I felt sure that it was a favourite for both of us.

'But the child cannot be baptised by that name. It has to be a proper name,' he said. 'So, you could call her Kathleen or Katherine. Either would be acceptable.'

I felt uncomfortable with this. Acceptable by the church, I supposed. What about what was acceptable to her parents? I respectfully asked why she couldn't be called Katy, and he responded by saying that it was a nickname. But another nagging question in my mind was why he had raised the prospect of a baptism at this early stage.

I soon discovered. He said that it was normal for a child to be baptised very quickly following birth, and that he had it in his diary to perform it in three days' time.

I didn't have the courage to question this. Once again, I felt that the church was dominating my whole birthing experience. I didn't understand why there was such a need to do this quickly. Was it because I was a Protestant in a land of Catholicism, and therefore there was a need to strike quickly while I was vulnerable and in no position to formulate alternative arrangements?

There came another stipulation. I had to decide upon at least one other, middle name. I said that I had not discussed that yet with my husband and that, perhaps, I could do so later that evening. I wanted to keep the priest at bay while I thought about all of this, and had spoken to Sean about it.

Sean arrived at seven o' clock that evening. This time he had managed to stay reasonably sober. We both set aside our differences of the previous day while I put my concerns to him. He didn't have any answers.

'Sue, I told you all about the power of the church here before we came. Is it such a big deal, after all? It's a small ceremony that keeps them happy. And as for her name, well, we can name her Katherine, as he's suggested. That's for official purposes. We'll just call her Katy, because that's her name to us.'

I decided that there was nothing I could do, but to accept the situation as it stood. There would be no one to support me if I had wanted to oppose anything that Father O'Connor were to insist upon, and so I consoled myself with the fact that it would all mean very little to me anyway. We agreed to Katy's middle name being Jane. I asked Sean to call at John's Street to collect my green two-piece suit and a nice blouse that I could wear to the service.

The following evening, Sean struck another blow, the subject of which must have arisen from Mary's need to warn me of something else.

'You do know, Sue, that you won't be allowed to attend Katy's baptism, don't you?' Sean said, looking distinctly awkward.

'What? No, that can't be right,' I exclaimed. 'I'll be barred from my own daughter's baptism? You are joking, aren't you?'

'It's just the way it is, Sue. Things are different here, in this country.' He looked awkward and apologetic.

'Who says?'

'The church. I can check with the priest, if you like, or maybe I could ask at the desk outside, but I know what the answer will be.'

Sean disappeared for some time. When he returned he said that Father O'Connor wasn't available but he said that there was another cleric, a seminarian, whatever that was.

'He confirmed that you won't be expected to attend.'

'Did you ask him why?'

'Look, Sue, I was brought up not to ask a priest questions like this. No, I didn't. There's no point in arguing with a priest. They'll have our family marked out as disrespectful and having problems. Anyway, I hope you'll understand why I didn't bring your suit here from the flat?'

I slumped back into my pillows. Was it because I am Protestant? Or maybe they view me as 'unclean', in not yet having been pronounced by the church to be 'purged' of all my birthing fluids? Either way it was all totally unjust.

The morning arrived for Katy's baptism. I gently sponged her beautiful body and combed her hair, including her signature curl, and then dressed her in a pretty frock, and finally wrapped her in a special white shawl that Mary had sent. Sean arrived in his best suit, and I kissed her and handed her over to him, feeling ostracized from my own dear baby's naming ritual and blessing.

I felt bereft, and powerless.

About an hour later Sean returned, bringing Katy back on his own. I imagined that the whole family, dressed in their Sunday best, with the women in their black veils, might have felt embarrassed or guilty that I hadn't been allowed to go to my own daughter's baptism whilst *they had.* Perhaps it was thought better for them to slip away quietly without seeing me, just in case I had something to say about it. Besides, there'll be some celebrating at Docherty's this lunchtime and afternoon for everyone, I felt sure, except me.

I didn't need a liquor bar to celebrate my daughter. I held her in my arms, knowing that I was the only true beneficiary of this precious life I held. No one else could ever give her the love and care during her lifetime that I would gift to her. Such was the overwhelming love I had for both of my babies that I would be prepared to give up my own life if it meant that theirs would be spared. That's all that mattered. That I would love them equally, and above everything else for the rest of my life.

CHAPTER 15

Stepping out of a taxi in John Street with Sean I became aware of several people in the street, and the Pharmacy itself, stopping to witness my return, holding our new daughter. For Sean to have summoned a taxi to bring us home was a kindness and I presumed that all was well.

'So, there's no work today?' I asked him.

'No, I did tell you that the work at the farm was temporary. I've been staying in Fintan Street for the last week, and I've put out another word that I'm looking for work again. I will get something, Sue. I promise.'

I felt despondent at hearing this, but no news of this sort surprised me any more.

Back home in John Street with my baby daughter, I was eager to see Jimmy again. Ten days is a long time for an infant of twelve months to be separated from his mother, and I wanted to reconnect with him and check that all was well with him.

'Will Mary be bringing Jimmy back to us here in John Street?' I asked him.

'No, I think she's busy today, so I'll go back over and collect him.'

'Well how about we go over to Fintan Street together and take Katy to show everybody? Then we can both collect him?'

241

'It's okay,' he said. 'I have to collect the list of fixtures anyway from Paddy O'Rourke up Barracks Road, so I might as well just collect him and bring him back here.'

'Oh, okay. Please thank your mum and all the family for looking after him,' I said, but I secretly wondered whether the incident at the hospital had created another storm with Mary, and that she had perhaps been less than forgiving.

Mary had lived a very hard life. Her face was deeply etched with the lines and lack of definition that one might expect to see in a seventy five year old rather than a woman more than twenty years younger. Having had so many pregnancies, and a life defined by the strictures of poverty, not only was her physical being ravaged, but her mental state also, characterized by angry outbursts of shouting and swearing, told to me by Sean many times over. I actually felt a great deal of compassion for her, and for all women who had been similarly forced to comply with an ethic which forbade all forms of birth control, and particularly so in a country where there was little help for the poor.

I became determined that my future would not be determined by any religious ideology. My rest in hospital had given me some time to think ahead about how I should proceed. My family was complete, I decided, and I toyed with the idea of visiting a doctor, whose surgery I had passed many times at the top of John Street, on a stretch of road known as The Parade. The brass plaque outside stated his name as Dr Percival, and I had long since mused that, to my ears, this didn't sound like one of the traditional Irish names. I wondered whether he might be Protestant and, as such, hold differing views about contraception to those of Catholic doctors. One day, as I queued up in the greengrocer's, I felt as though I were being handed a trump card; I overheard an older woman who was buying some green beans whisper to the lady serving, whom I had come to know as Eileen:

'Well, I hear that Dr Percival has given Bridget O'Donoghue *the pill,* would you believe? As you well know, she's already had seven children and I hear that she spent time up in the Sanatorium at the Boreen near Bennettsbridge. They say that, another baby, and she'll be threatening to hang herself!'

I wasn't about to hang *myself,* but I could sympathise with Bridget.

I plucked up the courage to make an appointment to see Dr Percival. A man in his middle years, I was struck by his kindly face.

I sat nervously at the other side of his large oak desk.

'Doctor, I've come to ask you for some help. I have been married only a short while, and I have two beautiful children. I am Protestant, and my husband is Roman Catholic. My husband knows that I am coming to see you, and he approves of my reasons for doing so. However, our marriage isn't a stable one. He spends a good deal of time out of work, in preference to playing handball and drinking heavily. I don't think that our marriage is going to survive, though I do try very hard to make things work. We are still together, however, and I have come to ask you if you will kindly consider prescribing the pill for me, so that I don't have any more children. I love both my babies, but I really don't want any more now.'

Dr Percival listened carefully and, without any hesitation, and thus obviating the need for any ingratiating pleas on my part, he lifted his pen and scribbled out a prescription, handing it to me over the desk. He went on to explain how I should take it, and that my periods would occur, almost as normal. I could have swivelled my ample, post-natal derriere over the desk to plant a great kiss on his cheek but maternal propriety and circumspection ruled the day. I thanked him profusely, departed the surgery, and made my way back down John Street to face my next challenge, that of having the pill dispensed in the very Pharmacy below our flat. I estimated that the news would reach the other end of town within the next twenty four hours.

Within days I began to question how much I needed birth control after all, because Sean's appearances became more and more erratic and infrequent. One week followed the next and there was no sign of him. I don't know how he imagined the three of us were going to eat.

I knew that the Republic of Ireland did not have a welfare benefit system such as that in the UK to help people who fell below the poverty line, but I had an inkling that there was some sort of food benefit for people in receipt of low incomes, for which I could apply.

I made enquiries and was advised to register with the city's welfare department for the poor. I was granted a weekly food token of two pounds which could be spent at one of several designated grocer's shops around the city. I chose one that stood a fair walk away, to try to avoid the gossip-mongers nearby finding out. I felt relieved because aid was regular, and I could buy provisions for the babies, whilst the remainder went on food basics of mainly bread, butter, tea, milk and potatoes for me.

Periodically, Sean would turn up, leave enough Irish pounds to pay for the rent only, followed usually by a row, or the whiff of one, and he would disappear at the speed of lightening on his way back to Fintan Street, and into his more gratifying world of handball. I had a suspicion that he was working very little, and playing handball in County matches.

I was becoming thinner, worrying about what was going to become of us, and eating inadequately. I was losing self-confidence, and I became dispirited about my life and how to deal with another, seemingly impossible situation again. During some weeks the food ran out and I had to go without some meals. My main consideration was always the children. I made sure that, if nothing else, they *never* went without.

One evening, when it was suitably dark enough, I wrapped my little ones up well against the cold, and took them downstairs to place them in their pram at the foot of the stairs. Pushing them out into the winter's night I made my way down the deserted high street to where I had seen a convent at the other end of town. I knocked on the convent door and waited, anxiously. I was greeted by one of the nuns who asked what she could do for me.

'Sister, I'm so sorry to call at this time of night, but I'm on my own with two small babies and I'm very hungry. I would be grateful for anything that you could give me, anything at all, please.' She paused, to take stock, and stared into my desperate face.

'Wait there, now' she said, and closed the door again. I took a few steps backwards, into the gravel drive, and checked that Jimmy and Katy were both still asleep. Six or seven minutes passed and the nun reappeared with a cardboard box full of basic foodstuffs. I could have wept with gratitude.

'Thank you, Sister,' I said, 'That's so very kind of you.'

'God Bless you, now, and goodnight.'

After three trips up and down the stairs to our flat in John's Street, two for each baby, and one for the provisions, I settled them down again; Katy in the cot, and Jimmy in the bed where he would lie next to me, holding on to my long hair for comfort. That night, the tea and toast tasted especially good. It was the food of kindness.

I saw Sean less and less, and he would push the rent money under the door with barely enough frequency to keep Malachy Dooley at bay. I resorted more and more to begging, travelling to different convents so that I wouldn't become a nuisance to any one order of nuns. I found that I needed a little more help about every four weeks or so, and sometimes I asked for money, and at other times I asked for food. Any money that I could save I put towards another week's rental payment, but mostly I needed to buy food to fill my hungry frame.

I was sure that people were talking about me. Lone mothers were unusual. Women struggling to feed their children and themselves were usually supported by family, but I had none to turn to. People knew that my husband wasn't around for most of the time. Queuing up one day in the bakery for a loaf of bread a local woman, whose face I recognised, approached me:

'And how are you getting on now with the *two* babies?'

'Oh, it's all going very well, thank you. The baby sleeps through the night now and our little boy is just walking, and he's becoming a real chatterbox.'

'And how is your husband?' she asked. I sensed that she knew very well that he was an absentee spouse.

'Well he works away in the building trade, and I'm afraid I see him much less that I would like to, but at least he keeps the wolf from the door, I'm pleased to say.'

I realised that she might know differently. Someone that *she* knew might have been in the shop where I use the food voucher, and I didn't think, for a minute, she believed me. Others will have learned from Malachy Dooley that we were always in arrears with the rent, or heard him pounding on our door when I had nothing to give him, or couldn't face having to make up another round of lies and excuses.

It was nineteen-seventy. I had begged for help at almost every convent in and around the city, of which there were many. To try to avoid people becoming aware of my movements I went out to beg in the evenings when the light had fallen and most people were indoors. I had also called at many of the churches to ask the priests if they would kindly consider giving me a small sum of money for some food, including on one occasion from the Bishop of Kilkenny himself, as he came straight out of mass from the Cathedral one Sunday morning. I gathered my courage:

'Your Grace, would you please kindly spare me a minute? I feel so desperate. I'm so sorry, but I need to ask for your help.'

The Bishop stopped swirling incense, held out his hand to me and said:

'Kiss my ring.' I bent over to kiss the large, ornate ring on his hand.

'Please, Your Grace, I have two small children lying in the pram over there. I am on my own, and I am very hungry. Could you please spare me a pound to buy some food? I would be so grateful to you.'

I knew that he wouldn't have any money on his person, but he turned to another cleric nearby and whispered to him, presumably to instruct him to go and get something. As we waited, he asked my name and where I lived. He also asked me where my husband's family lived. His aid returned and he handed me an Irish five pound note, a sum which was considered a large amount of money in those days.

'May God be with you,' he said, making the sign of the cross towards my head and face.

I thanked him, and lowered my head in reverence, as he continued with his onward procession.

I didn't want to take my 'begging bowl' to the same clerics more than once, if I could help it, and there seemed to be only one place left where I might try, that of an old convent that was a good distance away out of the city, deep into the countryside.

One bitterly cold night in February, when temperatures had dropped well below zero, having eaten only the smallest piece of bread all day, I felt particularly hungry and desperate. I wrapped up all three of us and set off for the isolated convent.

I walked about two miles through the dark, unlit countryside, pushing the pram and following a road which I believed, and hoped, led to the convent. Not a soul, nor a vehicle, passed me that night, such was the cold. I didn't have the benefit of a good warm coat; I was dressed only in a three-quarter length light jacket, and I felt the icy north wind searing through my clothes and chilling me to the bone.

The convent emerged through the darkness of the ice cold, bleak night and I was never so glad to have reached my destination as I was on that evening. I was invited into a large farmhouse-type kitchen, along with the pram and my little family in it, where there was a huge roaring fire. The nuns all flocked around to see their evening visitors, and they peered into the pram to look at my darling children.

'Here you are, now,' one kind nun said, carrying a tray with a steaming hot mug of tea and a small plate of biscuits to try to warm my trembling body. She placed it down by the hearth carefully.

'Holding the mug tightly in one hand, as I chomped on the biscuits that evening, I felt overwhelmed by these women's kindness, and care. They were good women.

'This is so very kind of you all, Sisters. I can't thank you enough.'

'God bless you,' said one of the nuns, whilst I was asked by others where I lived, how old my babies were, and where I came from originally. Another nun handed me a cardboard box in which she had placed a loaf of bread, some butter from a local dairy, and quite a number of basic foodstuffs.

I left this secluded convent, sustained by refreshments and warmth and feeling nourished by love, and the knowledge that there were, still, lots of good people in the world.

The long walk back chilled me in a way that I have never since felt such pain. The frost bit through my fingers and toes, and cut through my entire body.

Once up the stairs to the flat, with Katy back in her cot, and Jimmy sleepily lying in the bed, ready for me to take off his fleecy hat, coat and mittens before restoring him to sleep, I broke down completely, and my face fell against his coat in great sobs.

This moment was the veritable 'straw that broke the camel's back'. I knew that I couldn't go on living like this any more. The strain and distress which I now felt daily poured into my toddler's fleecy coat, and I kissed him and lay him down to sleep.

'Mama's alright now,' I blubbered, tears dripping from my face. 'I have a new plan.'

Swallowing my pride again, I wrote to my parents and asked them if they could lend me some money; a small sum which I promised to repay when I got back on my feet. I hinted also that I was considering a return to Manchester at some point in the near future. The truth was that I had already decided to go, but I needed enough money to pay for my single ticket, first to Dublin, then on to the ferry to Holyhead in Wales, and onwards by train to Manchester.

By return, my father sent me the sum of eight pounds. He knew that I would pay him back as soon as I was able to. I hid the money down the back of a drawer until I could plan my escape. And it would be exactly that, because in nineteen-seventies' Ireland no wife would be allowed to take away the children of an Irish man without having to fully account for it.

Despite all the disadvantages of living in a country lagging far behind that of the UK in its attitudes, the dominance of the church and its slow economic development, I didn't want to leave Ireland. I loved the warmth of the Irish, their humour, kinship and rich heritage. However, I had no doubt in my mind that I needed to leave my feckless husband. I toyed with the idea that if I could stay in Ireland to accommodate visits from the babies' father, and especially for my children to enjoy the simpler life here, that would be the ideal situation. I scoured the classified advertisements in the Irish Times to try to find a resident housekeeper position which I might secure, and in which I could take my children.

Nothing came of it, except for two telephone calls in which single, older men dubiously offered me the job without even wishing to meet me. I suspected from their respective discourse that they would probably expect much more than simply house-keeping duties, in exchange for their 'generosity' in agreeing to take in two children also.

I was really trying to put off making that final, gargantuan break. I wanted a miracle to happen in which Sean would realise what he had waiting in John Street and try to make amends, prac-tical and emotional. But I knew that miracles were the stuff of dreams. I had to search for a better life, a fulfilling one in which the three of us could flourish and find happiness. I decided that the best time to leave would be in spring.

In the meantime I had to survive. Surprisingly, I discovered the location of a small convent which had hitherto escaped my attention, situated in the city itself down a small winding street just off the high street, a relatively short walk from our flat. How it had eluded me before now I had no idea but its small, incon-spicuous facade appeared to conceal an extensively long interior. I decided to keep it in mind until I felt desperate enough to need to go and ask for help again.

I found each experience of begging for food or money, as diffi-cult as the first time. Begging was rare, and regarded not only as unsavoury but as a public nuisance. Only hunger and necessity helped me to dilute the feelings of shame, anxiety and embarrassment which I harboured constantly.

It was a Saturday evening in late March. I had stretched my two pounds' worth of food voucher as far as it could possibly go that week, and I still had two more days before I could use my next voucher. The pureed food that I had bought for the children, now that Katy was almost six months old, plus some pain-relieving gel to help her with her teething, and some additional fresh fruit and vegetables for them both, meant that my own food allocation was more restricted than ever this week. I needed another loaf and a couple of potatoes to tide me over until I had a new voucher to spend on the following Monday.

I pushed the babies down the high street at an hour when people were generally settling down at the end of the day. This Saturday evening was particularly memorable because it was the night of The Eurovision Song Contest. The favourite to win was the UK's Mary Hopkin, one of the Beatles' proteges, but Ireland's new and upcoming singer, Dana, was also in the running, and so it seemed as if the whole city was rooting for Ireland's darling songstress. Mine was a far more fundamental preoccupation, as usual, that of managing to obtain some food; any food, to last for a few more days.

During this time I had lost all contact with Sean and had no means of being able to reach him.

The pram bumped along over the cobbles in the old part of the city. I knocked on the ancient convent door. It took a couple of hard knocks on the door before I was able to alert the attentions of the resident nuns. A young novice opened the door and, after asking her if they could possibly spare a loaf of bread and a few potatoes, she ushered me into the hallway, and invited me to bring in the pram also.

A surge of noise swelled from the sitting room next door, and I realised that the nuns were watching The Eurovision Song Contest; the volume of the television had been turned up high to allow the ageing nuns with hearing impairments to hear the songs comfortably.

The novice asked me to take a seat in the hallway. From where I was sitting, I could see through the open door. A large group of nuns in full habits and veils gathered around a tiny television set, all in state of great excitement, chattering and commenting upon the merits of each song. This sight melted my heart, as they waited for Dana to sing: 'All Kinds of Everything'.

I thanked the young nun for her box of provisions, and balanced it on the pram all the way home, imagining the nuns' cheers and claps as Dana performed for Ireland.

The next day I learned that Dana had actually won the contest! I was thrilled. The Irish people I knew were, in the main, naive, innocent and 'the salt of the earth', all having descended from the impoverishment, strife, and domination of English rule.

April came, and with it a visit from Sean, bearing more rent money. He came in and we shared a cup of tea. I felt heavy-hearted because I knew what I had soon to do. He lifted up his children, one by one, kissed them, and marvelled at their growth and development, chatting to them as if they would remember who he was.

Sean pulled out of his jacket the previous week's 'Kilkenny People' newspaper and thumbed through it, looking for a particular article to show me. He folded the page backwards and showed me a large photograph and write up. It read: 'All-Ireland's Number One Handball Player'. And there he was, with that beautiful smile of his, raised high upon the shoulders of male supporters, and waving a large trophy in the air.

I congratulated him, and now understood where he had been for the last six months, competing through County heats towards a final that took place far away from our city. As usual, I had no idea where he had found the money for the rent, and I didn't ask.

I was nervous, and subdued, because I had to tell him what I planned to do.

'Look, Sean,' I said, 'now the handball season has come to an end, please come back, just for a few weeks. I have something to tell you, and it would be nice for you to spend some time with Jimmy and Katy.'

'Well, why don't you pour me another cup out of that teapot, Sue, and tell me all about it now,' he said.

We sat in the kitchen, perched on our makeshift stools, supping tea.

'Sean, it's not working. *We're* not working.' He looked down at the floor, shifting awkwardly; anticipating what was to come.

'I've had to struggle so much over this past winter. You must know that it's been very hard for me.' He didn't answer, and swallowed hard, waiting for me to say more.

'We'll be leaving in two weeks' time. I'm heading for Manchester, but I don't know where we'll end up. I will write to you, though, and let you know where we are. You can come and see us, whenever you wish.'

I wiped away my tears, and searched into his tear-filled eyes. He was distressed. He must have known that this was coming, though, and he appeared to accept my decision without argument.

'Jesus Christ, Sue, Mammy's going to go spare.' He choked back his tears.

I thought this was a strange thing to say, because, other than on the day of Katy's birth I had not seen or heard from her. I knew that she was protecting her son whom, in her eyes, could do no wrong.

'She'll get the Priest, you know that don't ye, to try to stop ye.'

I didn't tell him that, in my desperation, I had telephoned the Bishop of Kilkenny at the end of last month and, after several attempts to reach him, his housekeeper finally answered the telephone and transferred the call to him. I reminded him of our brief meeting when I had pleaded for his help as he came out of the Cathedral swirling incense, and chanting. I confessed to him that I was contemplating doing the unthinkable: I was planning to leave my husband.

I wanted to receive his blessing. He gave me not only *his* blessing, but God's too: he said that from what he knew of the Delaney family, Sean would never be able to give me and our children the stability we needed. He advised me to go home, and said that I would be better off being back with my family. On that score, I knew that he was wrong. But the Irish are so family orientated that it was a forgivable misconception of his, and I thanked him for his advice and understanding.

I asked Sean if he was going to tell Mary.

'I'll try not to, but I'm telling ye, if this gets out, all hell will break loose and she'll get Father O'Callaghan to stop ye. She'd even go as far as to turn up at the railway station with the Priest if she thought she could put a stop to it.'

I believed him, but I had to take that chance, and hope that he wouldn't say a word of it to any of his brothers or sisters, particularly when he had too much to drink.

'So,' I asked, 'will you move back in, just to be with the children for a few weeks, and for us to end this on good terms?'

He flung his arms around me, and pulled me close to him, rocking me like a baby.

'I'm sorry, Sue, for everything,' he said, his face red with anguish, and tears streaming down his face. 'I'm no good for you, I know it. I do love you, and I love my babies.'

I cried too. I was tired and emotionally fragile with the mess of it all. But any feelings that I still held for him had become irrevocably subsumed by the overwhelming priority that lay towards our children. I wanted them to grow up well-nourished, emotionally stable, educated and with all the opportunities that I could possibly provide for them. *I* wanted a better life too. And if I were to stay I knew that our chances of a good life would always be a distant dream. I had to go.

The next two weeks passed as if in the blink of an eye. Sean was incredibly loving, and talked a lot about coming over to see us, and how much he would miss us.

I packed up our belongings, and managed to buy enough baby foods to see us through another week. I had our clothes, a good supply of Terry towelling nappies, some pots and pans and other practical items, all packed into two enormous suitcases. I also had a large bag of baby supplies, and a lightweight toddler's trolley so that I could at least push Jimmy, while I carried six month old Katy in my arms. How I would be able to manage the whole lot I couldn't imagine but, for a start, I had booked a taxi to take us the short distance down John Street to Kilkenny's railway station, where I knew that the driver would help to carry all of our belongings on to the platform. For the rest of the journey I had to look heavenward.

I also had to hope that I would be able to get on to that train unimpeded by Sean's family, or clergy summoned in for reinforcements.

The night before our departure from this beloved city Sean cradled each of us in his arms. He was tender towards me, and loving. Unable to watch us go, he left early in the morning, his face awash with tears. It was the end. He was unable to do the right thing by us.

I dressed my babies ready in their best clothes. They didn't understand what was happening, of course. They just knew that their Mama was with them, and I told them that we were going to be fine. I told them over and over how much I loved them, and that I would do, forever more.

The taxi arrived on time. I sensed eyes peering out between curtains and blinds as my suitcases were lifted into the boot of the taxi. My heart was racing. It took only three minutes to get to the station. I tipped the driver and asked him if he would kindly lift our suitcases on to the single, outward bound platform that constituted the end of the line. I waited with great trepidation for the train to approach, constantly looking over my shoulder at the open space where people drifted in from the ticket office.

I now needed to summon the courage of my life, in readiness for any obstruction to my plans that might happen. I was frightened. I knew that if anyone were to grab my precious children, then I would have to stay too, and any dreams of a better life for us would die on that platform.

The train approached. I lifted Jimmy out of the trolley and quickly collapsed it, stacking it next to the cases. I gripped his little hand in mine and held Katy firmly in my arms. I felt as if my heart was going to burst. Will Mary, or Father O'Callaghan rush through the entrance at any moment, waving and shouting? I was quaking at the thought that we had to get on that train as quickly as possible.

As the doors of the train were opened I moved quickly and steadfastly with my children as we stepped up, then I pulled back the sliding door of the carriage. I lifted both of my children, in turn, on to the nearest seat at the back of the carriage. Katy had only recently learned how to sit up independently, and I had to take a chance on leaving them for a few minutes while

I went back out to lift in the suitcases and the trolley but, as I turned, a kind man was already boarding the train and lifting my cases into the corridor. He went back to retrieve the trolley for me and then heaved all three items on to the overhead luggage compartment.

'There, now, is that alright for ye?' he smiled, glancing at my children. I shook his hand and thanked him for his kindness, as my little ones glanced over to where I stood.

With Katy now on my lap I hugged Jimmy close to my side, sandwiched between me and the window, but my eyes were fixed through the glass at the entrance to the platform.

'Please train, please go!' I willed. My pounding heart seemed to suspend my breath. It was the longest five-minute wait I'd ever experienced.

The whistle blew. The carriage jerked, and the train made its snail-like departure out of the station, and into the open air of the county.

We were on our way.

We were leaving Ireland, this beautiful country that I had come to love. I was leaving my husband and the father of my children. Choked with loss and grief, I vowed to return one day to these shores. I had no idea what was going to happen to us, but I believed that there had to be a way of forging a new life for us; a good life; of kindness and love, and opportunity.

CHAPTER 16

It was a long journey. As I had anticipated, train and boat connections proved to be challenging. However, I had not bargained on Katy, almost seven months old, being unable to settle throughout the whole journey, due to teething problems. Trying to console her was stressful, as I wandered up and down the carriage, rocking her to and fro; it didn't allow any of us to rest, but eventually we arrived in the centre of Manchester, where I telephoned my parents' house.

It was late Sunday afternoon, 26th April nineteen-seventy.

I knew that Dad would be at home and, as usual, he answered the telephone.

'Hello Dad, it's Susan. I'm in Manchester. I'm at Mosely Street bus station with the children.'

'Alright, love. I'll be about half an hour, and I'll see you then.'

I was slightly unnerved by the almost matter-of-fact way in which he'd answered.

'Okay, Dad, look forward to seeing you. Bye.'

He hadn't seemed surprised, and there were no questions asked. Since my letter to him some weeks ago in which I hinted that we may return, I wondered whether he had not only anticipated our arrival, but also prepared his responses.

I was looking forward to seeing my parents again, and my sister Kay, and I hoped that they would especially want to see the new member of the family. Having left England a year ago when Jimmy was only six months old, my parents had never seen their granddaughter, Katy. I hoped that they would let us stay, if only for some weeks while I looked for somewhere for us to live.

As I waited, I wondered how Dad could have anticipated such a brief travel time, given the bus timetable and having to cross Manchester to reach us. However, it was only when he pulled up in a Vauxhall Viva that I realised just how; he had obviously been taking driving lessons and, having passed his test, bought a car.

He got out of the car.

'Hello love. You and the children go and sit in the back and I'll put these in the boot.' Curt and practical.

After putting our cases and the trolley into the boot of the car he got into the driver's seat again. Rummaging in a bag in the front passenger seat he lifted out a plastic container filled with warm milk. I started to feel uneasy.

'Your mum said that you might need this,' he said, handing me the capsule.

A horrible feeling was dawning on me.

'You can't stay with us, love. We have no room, and we lead very busy lives. As you know, we're still living over shop premises. Your mum runs the shop and I go out to work.'

I fell silent. After the events of the last year I was in a fairly poor state of health and, although I had always been slim, I had lost a lot of weight. My defences were at an all time low. I waited for his next pronouncements.

'Wasn't there a nun in Victoria Park somewhere, who once helped you?'

My heart sank.

'Yes,' I answered quietly. 'Sister Augustine.'

'Well, I think that she's probably the best person to help you now. We'll drive to Victoria Park, and let me know when we're near where she lives.'

My whole being lapsed into quiet submission. I wrapped my arms around my little ones, holding them close to me, defensively, fearing what might happen.

It was nothing less than a massive body blow. History was repeating itself: It wasn't the first time I had contacted my parents for help and Dad handed me over to an authority. His decision was absolute, whether I resided in the family unit, or not. I was not in a position to oppose it, or to argue. Further, that would only serve to strengthen his resolve.

The silence throughout the short drive to Victoria Park and along Anson road was punctuated only as we neared the park as Dad queried:

'Is it around here?'

'If you stop here, we're near enough,' I said, pointing to a wall next to a strip of land.

He pulled up, and quickly walked round to the boot of the car while I manoeuvred the children out of it, together with our belongings, on to the pavement. Deeply shocked and hurt, my face must have told as much.

I fastened Jimmy in the trolley and, whilst levering my large bag in the crease of my elbow, and holding Katy firmly to me with my left arm, I heaved one of the heavy cases towards me by the handle, grabbing the trolley, simultaneously, with my right hand.

Dad had one final thing to say.

'It's best not to ring home. Your mum's very busy, what with the shop, and all. But you can drop us a line when you're settled somewhere.'

I couldn't look at him.

'Please leave the other case just over there by the wall, and I'll come back for it in a few minutes,' I murmured.

I turned towards the convent which stood about a hundred yards away, and struggled, with every last ounce of strength I had, to propel forwards with all of my load.

I deposited the bag and suitcase in the drive of the convent, took several deep breaths and returned with my little ones to collect the second large suitcase, to repeat the same haul again.

There was no sign of Dad now.

And he hadn't even beheld his beautiful grandchildren.

I stood for a few moments in the drive of the big house, trying to catch my breath, and gather my momentum. This was no time for distress. No time to lick wounds. What if Sister Augustine wasn't available? What could I say to her *anyway*? That my father has just dropped me off? That my parents couldn't help us, or didn't want to? No, I decided. I couldn't tell her that. I felt deeply ashamed; deeply hurt and humiliated. Dad had rejected me again, only this time with two young children.

For the third time I stood in front of the familiar door about to ask for help.

A young nun opened the door.

'Hello, I'm Susan, and I'm wondering if Sister Augustine might be available to see me, please?' My voice quaked and I swallowed hard, so as not to cry.

The young woman stared for a moment, as I held the tiny hand of my toddler, and clutched my baby in my arms. She smiled. It was hard *not* to smile at these two beautiful, innocent faces.

'Why don't you step inside, and I'll go and check for you?'

Sitting in the familiar Victorian hallway with its original black and white chequered tiles, I placed Jimmy in the upright chair next to me, and sat Katy on my lap.

Several minutes later the now, slightly bent figure of the elderly, Irish nun appeared through a nearby door, and beckoned me inside the same adjoining room where I had last pleaded for help. It had been twenty months ago, when she placed me in a Home for Unmarried Mothers in Prestwich, run by Catholic nuns.

I summoned a voice, and my adrenalin-fuelled acting skills kick-started. RADA would have been impressed.

'Hello, Sister Augustine. It's so nice to see you again. I hope you're well,' I said.

'I am indeed, Susan. And how are you, and what can I do for you now?'

'Thank you for seeing me Sister. This is my little boy Jimmy, who is eighteen months old, and this is my little girl, Katy, who is six months old. She was born in Kilkenny, in Ireland.'

With some trepidation as to how the rest might come out, I continued:

'I married their father, and he struggled to stay in work. Our relationship was turbulent, to say the least. After some time we went back to his home town in Ireland to try to make the marriage work. However, I found that he really didn't try very hard to find work there either. He was more interested in playing handball and frequenting the bars. I ended up regularly having to beg for food and money to keep us going. Well……….,' I paused to try to find the wherewithal to soften the impact of my words, but there was no other way I could think of telling her what, in her eyes, I knew, would prove unforgivable:

'I have left him, Sister Augustine, and I need a bit of help in finding somewhere to live. I wonder, Sister, would you please be able to help me?'

She was immediate, and forthright, in her response.

'Susan, your place is with your husband. You must go back over there to be with him,' she said, with apparent total conviction.

All that I could think, was that she was urging me, like Daniel, to go back into the lion's den again.

'Sister, I can't go back. The only reason he didn't resort to violence in Ireland was because of his fears of the Garda, and what they might do to him in the barracks. Crucially, also, his heart lay not with me and his children. He was an absentee husband, and our welfare was secondary to his own needs and wants.'

'I still say that your place lies with him. You married, and swore to the Holy Father, that you would remain his wife, for better or for worse, and they *are* his children, after all.'

I was in quicksand, flailing for my life.

'Sister, I beg you, please help us. The priests and the nuns were so kind and helpful towards me. They knew of our situation. Even the Bishop of Kilkenny advised me to leave Sean and to come back here. *Please,* Sister, do telephone him. He will remember me.'

She stared at me, thoughtfully, realising that I couldn't have made that up.

'Well, then, your parents must help you. You must go back to your family.'

I took another deep breath.

I couldn't possibly ask them,' I lied. 'They have very little room and they wouldn't be sympathetic. They're not compassionate people, and especially towards children.'

I couldn't tell her the truth; I felt the utmost shame; that, barely minutes before my arrival, my father had dumped all three of us practically on her doorstep.

I was panicking, for fear of a continued refusal to help me. I was in the presence of a figure of authority; completely at her mercy, and I found myself shaking at the thought of having to be on the streets. If we had no roof over our heads I risked Social Services taking my children into Care. The same would apply if I asked the police for help. I would be regarded as an unfit mother, and my little ones would be taken away. I couldn't bear the thought of it. I gulped hard, and began to hyperventilate, as I waited anxiously to hear how she would respond.

'Wait here,' she said and, with that, she left the three of us alone in the room. I looked into the eyes of my beautiful, innocent children. I loved these two little bodies more than anything in the whole world.

Both children looked around them, wide-eyed, and back again at their mama.

'It's okay, we're doing okay. Goodness, aren't you a good boy, and a good girl,' I comforted them, my body stricken with anxiety. I was also trying to reassure *myself* somehow too. Had Sister Augustine gone to telephone the Bishop of Kilkenny? At least, then, she would understand how desperate my situation had been.

The elderly nun came back into the room, carrying her car keys in her hand.

'I'm going to take you ………………….'

In that instant it was as if an enormous crane winched me out of the mire. She could take us *anywhere*. I listened carefully again.

'It's a Home, run by Social Services for women and children. The Matron is expecting us in about a half an hour.'

As the nun drove, she had very little to say this time, and I, in my depleted state, also had nothing left but to express my gratitude for her help, once more.

We headed out of Manchester on the main route through Rusholme towards Fallowfield. She turned right off the main road at a major crossroads and, minutes later, entered the drive of a large Georgian house where, above the door, writ large, was the name: 'Moorbank'.

Once inside we were handed over, like chattels, to a mature white-haired, po-faced woman who was the Matron-in-Charge. She led us upstairs to a first floor room overlooking the drive.

There was a double bed, a single bed and a set of drawers. Like the bleak hostel in Manchester where my father had once deposited me, there were thick iron bars fitted horizontally across the window. Yes, it was *another* institution, but I welcomed this small room which would be our new sanctuary; our harbinger of restoration.

As the matron closed the door behind her there were no tears this time. All my crying was done. There were three of us now, and the only way forward, I vowed, was up.

CHAPTER 17

Moorbank was a Home for destitute women and children, particularly for those fleeing from domestic violence. The doorbell rang at all times of the day and throughout the night as the police brought in what, at this time, were called 'battered wives', accompanied by their offspring, for safety. It might have partly explained the reason for Matron's pained expression, and her chain smoking proclivity. There was always a cigarette butt hanging out of the corner of her mouth, or perched on the edge of her desk. Not once did I ever see her smile. It must have been a grim job, taking in an endless stream of injured women, some needing medical assistance, and all in a state of trauma, to one extent or another.

The women of all ages came from different backgrounds and classes. This was to become an experience in which I gained another unique insight into a profoundly shocking, constant and disturbing reflection of gender injustice.

At that time my thinking around issues of 'class' was limited but I was markedly struck by the fact that many of the women *weren't* working class; and many weren't young. There were significant differences in their levels of education and socio-economic backgrounds. At nineteen years old I was the youngest mother.

During that time I mixed with all of the women, as we ate together, shared communal bathrooms, undertook domestic chores together and sometimes shared child care responsibilities. We sluiced and laundered our babies' nappies together in the basement, exchanging our fraught experiences, as women and mothers. There was great camaraderie between all of us; shared laughter, and occasionally tears, and an unspoken understanding of each other's suffering. It was sisterhood, all over again. None of us chose to be there, but we valued the respite from harm's way and the chance to re-evaluate our circumstances.

On one particular occasion, I was waiting my turn to use the bathroom to wash my children and prepare them for bedtime while a woman in her forties was washing her daughter's hair. The mother was extremely thin, with a pallid complexion and shoulder-length, lank hair. Notably, she had very few teeth, and after she had spoken of many years of being forced out on to the streets by her live-in, violent spouse, I understood why. What surprised me, however, was the pride with which she described her decades-long prostitution, and of making enough money to be able to keep a roof over her family's head and provide them all with food and clothes.

I made friends in particular with two women: Joan, who had two children and who was brought in late one night by the police, battered and bleeding, and Pauline, who had three young children with her, having reluctantly left three older boys with her husband. Joan was a middle class housewife, and her high-earning husband, and perpetrator, remained in what she described as her beautiful large home in Swinton. Pauline was a hard working woman who was originally from Ghana. She had worked as a cleaner to fit in with the children's schooling, though she was well educated and had suffered for some years at the hands of a bully who worked little, and drank heavily, and who beat her regularly. Both women were considerably older than me, but we shared common ground and got on well with each other. Pauline and I corresponded for quite a while after leaving the Home, such was our mutual respect and friendship.

All meals were provided by the Home, and residents were asked to go to matron's office every Friday where she would hand each of us one pound, which was our allocated spending money arising from the Social Services' benefit claim made on our behalf.

I soon learned that some of the women had lived in the Home for many months and, in some instances, considerably more than a year. It was expected that residents would join local authority housing lists, and petition, individually, to be offered self contained accommodation. Although I joined one such list I felt that waiting to be offered a council property could take a long time, and I was keen to try other means also of finding somewhere for us to live.

I soon resolved to get out every single day to try to see if I could find suitable accommodation. This became my mission. Moorbank had several, donated old prams which the women were free to use if they wanted to take out their young children, and so, daily, I borrowed a sturdy old Silver Cross pram in which I could comfortably place, at either end, my two growing infants.

I became familiar with the large residential areas of Fallowfield, Withington and Didsbury, where there were many sizeable old properties that were divided into small flats, or sometimes single rooms to let. It didn't take me long, however, to realise the extent of prejudice and discrimination which was endemic within our suburbs. I witnessed, on a grand scale, many large, handwritten signs, on doors, on gates, and sometimes at the end of a row of houses, which stated boldly:

'NO BLACKS
NO IRISH
NO SINGLE MOTHERS'

After two months of relentless daily searching on foot, literally pounding the streets of large nearby boroughs, and 'cold calling' on many properties, I obtained a clear picture of the private lettings market and how it was nigh impossible, as a member of a minority group, to rent privately. One day, despite seeing one of the large notices warning that I was not welcome, I knocked on the door of a large villa-type residence, and waited. A woman in her fifties opened the door.

'Good morning,' I ventured. She nodded, and waited for me to continue. 'I've seen your sign, and I must admit that I *am* *a* single mum of two young children. They are both extremely well behaved and I would never, ever, default on my rent. Might you have a room to let, or a studio flat? I'd take great care of the property, and I can assure you that I'd be a good tenant.'

The woman looked me up and down and replied, tersely,

'No, I can't help you,' and she slammed the door shut.

Property owners were just one cohort of many who tended to judge people in terms of the stereotypes they read about in the press at that time; certain 'types' who threatened to de-stable the status quo within society; in this instance, single mothers who were associated with the rising number of 'broken families', as if it was all their fault.

Women's Aid was founded four years' later, bringing together the newly formed women's refuges, and it initiated widespread campaigns to educate and to lobby for new laws and policies to protect women and children living with violence and abuse.

Unlike refuges today, Moorbank gave no advice or support to women about housing, employment, how to access services, or cope with the distress which many of the women and children were experiencing.

As a resident of the Home, I nevertheless regarded myself as very fortunate in having been given a sanctuary, and thus an opportunity to take stock and start anew. On a personal level, it was a time of great hope and expectation, and of feeling gradually more confident that we would soon be on our way towards a better life. Hope sprang eternal.

After two months I began to widen the net of my search, thumbing through telephone directories to look for leads, and calling in at the reference section of the local library in Platt Lane. I felt sure that there must be some religious organisations which might offer me some support in my search for somewhere to live. I read of an organisation which was based in central Manchester, in Albert Square, called The Catholic Family Welfare Society. I had no idea what sort of welfare it had at its purpose but I thought it might be a good place to visit in person. I set off with Katy and Jimmy one morning after breakfast to catch the bus into town.

In the square there was a sign above a small office, not far from the Town Hall. I entered, and walked up to a counter, behind which sat a young woman at a typewriter.

'Could you please tell me if anyone might be available to discuss with me a matter of importance regarding myself and my family?'

'Let me see,' she said, rising from her swivel chair. 'I'll just see if Father Peter is available for you.'

There was a time, not so long ago, when the thought of having a meeting with a priest would have unnerved me but, in recent years, having had conversations with nuns, vicars, priests and even a Catholic Bishop, whilst far from claiming to be a 'doyen' of such encounters, neither was I worried about the prospect.

The young woman returned and lifted up part of the counter, ushering us through into the main office. She led us onwards into a much pokier office at the back where a young priest wearing a black shirt with dog collar, and sleeves rolled up to his elbows, was smoking a cigarette, and pivoting backwards on just two legs of his chair.

'Hello there,' he said, promptly restoring his front chair legs to terra firma, and pushing the door closed behind me to allow for some privacy. 'Please take a seat. And who have you got there with you?'

'Well, Father Peter, this is Jimmy, who is twenty one months old, and this is Katy, who is just nine months old.'

I stared at this beautiful young man in front of me. He really was precisely that. He must have been in his late twenties. He had a shock of blonde, tousled hair and a smile so wide I was instantly mesmerized. He was almost a carbon copy of the well known, young American actor, George Peppard. What a pity he had given himself to the Lord, I thought.

'Tell me, Susan, how can I help you?'

'Father, I don't know where to begin, but I've had quite a journey.'

'Tell me about it,' he urged.

I started at the beginning, relating to him my father's harsh and aggressive behaviour towards me, which gave rise to my leaving home. That I quickly became pregnant and went with my boyfriend to London, where we were forced to live on the streets. I summarized my time in the convent in London; being beaten up by my boyfriend and returning to Manchester, only to be put into a hostel for the destitute by my father; being placed into another couple of institutions, one of which was a mother and baby home where I had to fight to keep my baby.

I went on to tell the Priest how there was no alternative for me to live with my child anywhere and the only real option

271

available to me was to marry the father of my baby. I glossed over my husband's 'underground activities', and told him about moving to Ireland; how my husband drank heavily and spent most of his days playing handball. On my own most of time, I had to resort to begging for food and money, at times, and how I eventually left him and came back to Manchester.

'I'm now living in a Home in Fallowfield for destitute women and children. I'm trying very hard to find somewhere for the three of us to live, but so far I've not been successful, though I go out every day, and try. The private housing market is prejudiced against women like me.' I hesitated. 'Father Peter, is there was any way at all that you might be able to give me some ideas as to how I can find accommodation, so that I can begin to make a home for us?'

The priest lit up another cigarette and leaned back precariously again in his chair, his hands behind his head, blowing out clouds of smoke into the air like some native American Indian chief in a pow-wow.

'Good Lord,' he said. 'If anyone ever deserved to be helped, it's you.'

He fell silent.

You could hear a pin drop.

He resumed: 'Let's start by taking your full name, and the address of the Home, and then leave it with me, Susan. I'll discuss it with a few colleagues, and I'll get back to you.'

I felt immediately heartened by his words. Even if nothing came of this, I thought, I felt so glad to have met such a lovely person; a man who was clearly trying very hard to give hope to people, and to families of disadvantage, who had none. I thanked him profusely for listening, and in anticipation of any advice he might suggest which could help us.

On the bus ride back to Fallowfield, uplifted by our meeting, how I wished that there were more grounded, approachable Father Peters in this world.

Some weeks passed since my meeting with Father Peter, and my stay at Moorbank was nearing its fourth month. One day, on a warm, sunny Sunday afternoon in late July, I was one of many homeless women who were sitting out with their children on the lawn at the back of the large house.

Joan had already left for the day with her children to visit her parents in Worsley. My other close friend, Pauline, and I chatted together while our children enjoyed the fresh air and played with balls and soft play equipment.

We looked around, suddenly aware of Matron coming out into the garden, shielding her eyes from the sun, whilst visibly trying to seek out someone from the crowd. She was accompanied by a figure I instantly recognised.

'Oh, it's Father Peter!' I exclaimed to Pauline, scrambling to my feet, and rushing over to greet the priest. Matron turned to go back indoors, as I held out my hand to shake the Priest's hand, in happiness and surprise.

'Father Peter. It's lovely to see you!'

'Susan, I have some great news for you!'

I stared at him wide-eyed, holding my breath, wondering.............

'We've found you a house! It's not up to much, but it's a house; a new start for you and your children.' He was smiling that wide, engaging smile of his.

Both my hands had already swept to my face, trying to stifle an exhilarated gasp of joy.

'Oh, that's wonderful; just wonderful! Oh my goodness! I just can't thank you enough, Father.'

'Now, would someone look after your children while I take you off to see it?'

I darted back to Pauline, dazed in shock and exhilaration.

'Can I ask you a big favour, Pauline? Could you please look after Jimmy and Katy for an hour or so, while I go with Father Peter? He has a place he wants me to see.'

Pauline was smiling too, having overheard the conversation. She was a good, generous-hearted woman.

'Off you go, and don't you worry about these little ones.'

I opened the door to the front passenger seat of Father Peter's clapped out old banger of a car, still feeling overwhelmed by the news; thinking that this must be the happiest day of my life.

'It's an old house, Susan, and it's not in great condition, but it's a start for the three of you. The Catholic Welfare Society has bought the house for you and we will rent it out to you,' he said, puffing hard on a cigarette.

'Father, I really don't mind at all what condition it's in. I'll do my best to do it up. I'm just so happy and grateful to you. A place of our own! Oh, goodness. Thank you so much!'

'It's in Patricroft. Do you know it?'

'I *do*, Father. My grandmother lived in Irlam, just a few miles away.'

Father Peter drove us across the city and through Eccles into the suburb of Patricroft. Set back off the main road in a small cul-de-sac, he parked outside number six, Lynwood Avenue. He unlocked the door of the old terraced property and we entered my long-awaited-for, new home.

'Take a look round,' said the priest. 'You'll see that it's a bit dilapidated; also, it has an outdoor toilet and, I'm afraid, no bathroom and no hot water plumbing, but it gets you out of the Home, and it's a start for you Susan.'

'Please don't apologise for anything. I'll manage. I'm just so grateful, and we'll be just fine. Thank you *so* much, Father.'

'We'll get you some second hand furniture, so that you have something to sit on, a few beds to sleep on, and the rest will be up to you. I'll give you our telephone number and perhaps we can co-ordinate your moving day with delivery of some bits and pieces.'

At last, we were finally on our way!

CHAPTER 18

Throughout our time at Moorbank, and subsequent move to Patricroft, there was no contact with my parents. It was as if they belonged solely to the past, in a far distant universe.

Father Peter, true to his word, sent delivery of two upright chairs, an old couch, and two beds, a single and a double. I must have been the only householder in the country who owned chairs with large hollow crucifixes carved into the back of them!

The first thing that I did was to order some coal, and when it arrived it had to be piled in a heap opposite the back door. It was customary for coal to be dropped into the cellar from an iron-lidded chute, located near the front door. However the cellar steps, accessed via the kitchen, were so badly eroded and uneven that I wasn't keen on the idea of going down into that dark, dank basement and having to haul up buckets of coal. I imagined the horror of losing my footing and falling into a heap on to the earthen floor below, unable to get up, and with two young children left upstairs, helpless and neglected. The alternative, unsatisfactory arrangement meant that my coal was left out in the open air, frequently drenched in rain, with the result that it was often very difficult to light the fire. With old copies of The Manchester Evening News held up against the fireplace to create a draught I always managed to do it, eventually.

Life was tough, but bearable. Now, with an independent address I could obtain social security benefits which were sufficient to pay for my rent, council rates, food for each week, and a little spare cash to put into the electricity meter. I detested, however, having to rely on state support.

Long before leaving school I had worked in various jobs. When I was fourteen, working alongside my mother at home I was employed throughout the summer holidays, machine sewing every day, making aprons as a homeworker. Not long afterwards, from aged fifteen to seventeen years old I had held various Saturday jobs, first as a packer in a factory with John Myers' catalogue company, and then as a sales assistant in Manchester. For many years I had been an earner, and I wanted to bring up my children and support them myself but I knew that, if only temporarily, I had to rely on government help.

I budgeted carefully, planning basic but nutritious meals for each week, buying only what was required. Invariably, though, by Sunday my purse was empty and there was nothing left to put into the electric meter. Sunday evenings were often spent sitting in the pitch dark, with only the embers from the fire to sustain me.

Within weeks I had found a part time job where I could take my children. A local woman who ran a bed and breakfast, accommodating male students, was looking for a cleaner to come every weekday morning to undertake basic cleaning duties. She allowed me to take Jimmy and Katy along in their pram and leave them in her sitting room, where I would pop down frequently to check that they were happy, and busy playing with their toys, or sleeping.

The job was dismal but it earned me some extra money, which I was allowed to earn by the department of Health and Social

Security; money to buy children's clothes, and treats for them for birthdays and at Christmas.

The male students left their messes behind, including soiled toilet paper full of their previous night's 'pleasure', with adult magazines under the bed. I felt demoralised by the work, but I had experienced far worse. I did this for some months until a wonderful Social Worker, whom I had contacted for help, came to bring me the good news that she had secured two nursery places for my children in Irlam, a small town four miles away.

I was overjoyed. I thought it would provide necessary social and intellectual stimulation for Jimmy and Katy because, although I played with my children and read to them daily, I had no friends or family with whom they could interact. We had no callers.

Hastily, I set about trying to find a full time job. Because the nursery was a short bus drive away it made sense to try to look for a job near to the nursery. There were few opportunities available but I was fortunate in being interviewed for a job as a laboratory technician at the local Co-operative Margarine factory, testing fats and butters for salt. I was successful, and my working life as a single mother began in earnest.

The job was tedious, but I earned more than I would have received in claiming benefits.

Jimmy and Katy fared better than I: they were loved in the nursery, and they thrived, learning all sorts of new skills, enjoying experiences that I alone couldn't have provided, and their communication skills developed immeasurably.

Each day was challenging for me. Rising early, I provided a good breakfast for us all, washed and dressed my little ones and got myself ready, then we caught the bus into Irlam. Once they were in the nursery I could concentrate on my working day. I walked the short distance to the factory and, later on, collected my children and caught the bus home. My first task was to make a coal fire, after which I prepared supper, before getting the children ready for bed.

The house had no hot water system, and so every evening I boiled a kettle on the stove, and placed another kettle on the open fire, to provide enough hot water for Jimmy and Katy's bath in front of the fire in a large plastic bath. Once the children were in bed and fast asleep, I refilled the old blackened kettle with water and placed it on the coal fire again to boil, trying to keep electricity costs to a minimum, and added it to the used bathwater. The plastic bath was just about big enough to hold my bottom and feet, as I stared into the hot coals and contemplated our future.

Life was hard, but I gave myself permission to dream again of a better future to come.

Throughout my time at the laboratory I received a number of telephone calls from the Matron of the nursery to tell me to come and collect the children because one of them seemed to be unwell with a cold; and sometimes only had a slight runny nose. Each time I offered my apologies to my boss, and left work early to go and take them home. He became increasingly frustrated with my sudden, unplanned departures, which always left me feeling uncomfortable and guilty.

Relations with my parents seemed to be improving. Despite their aloofness towards me I desperately wanted my children to have some sort of a relationship with their grandparents. Living in this house, Mum and Dad visited us on a couple of occasions and stayed for a cup of tea. It was far from what I *would* have wanted, but I was grateful for any sort of contact with them.

The following year I spotted a vacancy in the wages department of The British Steel Works, which was situated two miles away from the nursery. I applied, and I was successful in being offered the job; it was better paid, and I hoped that the work would be more satisfying. However, on only the fifth day of my employment I discovered, to my utter dismay, that I was covered in red spots, and I was advised to see the Works' nurse. She promptly diagnosed German measles, and instructed me to go home!

I feared losing my job, but two weeks' later I was relieved to find that I still had one to return to.

I made contact with my parents during my illness, and on another, previous occasion also when I had acute tonsillitis. On both occasions my father answered simply that they would not visit because it would be bad for their business if they were to catch anything, and become ill themselves.

The loneliness and lack of support always felt emotionally crippling, but somehow I managed to cope.

The next big event in our lives was when, after petitioning the local council many times about my place on their housing list, I was offered the tenancy of a three-bedroomed maisonette which was situated on the outer edge of Irlam, overlooking farmland. It was in a lovely spot and there was a children's play park below our first floor home where I could watch my growing children play. Finally, we had a bathroom, hot water, *and* central heating. Sheer bliss!

At British Steel I gained promotion, becoming Timekeeper for the Civil Engineering Department, and the only woman employed on the Works itself. The all-male team comprised a great bunch of men who were very kind towards me. One member of staff, Arthur, happened also to be the Treasurer of the local branch of The British Legion Association and when the branch was undergoing refurbishment he rescued a small red table and four matching stools that would otherwise have been discarded. They looked perfect in our new kitchen!

On one very special day, not long after relocating, I received a letter informing me that I had been successful in my application to obtain a place at Manchester College of Higher Education, a Teacher Training College for mature students, affiliated to the University of Manchester. Coincidentally, the College was situated directly opposite the municipal hostel for destitute women on Long Millgate to which my father had taken me as a pregnant eighteen year old. It was also next door to the highly esteemed, Chetham's School of Music. This time I had landed on the right side of the road!

After a three-year, full-time course I spent eight years teaching in state schools in Greater Manchester and Salford, before moving on to various senior management positions in education and training establishments: on a US Army Base in Cheshire; in the Social Housing movement serving the East Midlands; and finally as Director of an Adult Education College in Wiltshire. Throughout these years, crucially also, I engaged in further part-time study, obtaining a BA degree in the Social Sciences, and a Master's degree in Women's Studies at the University of Lough-borough, both of which I undertook alongside full-time work, whilst bringing up Jimmy and Katy.

During all the years of my children's growing up I remained, happily, a single parent; the sole breadwinner, without financial assistance from any quarter, including that of Sean, whom we never saw again. From the very beginning, I knew that in order to provide the sort of opportunities I wanted my children to have I would need to advance my career in order to support them fully.

In the meantime, my two beautiful children grew up to be intelligent, creative and gifted young people, whose higher education I encouraged and supported financially, and in other ways. I became immensely proud of both of them. As we grew together, we developed a very close bond.

My journey had entailed one of the toughest, and yet most enlightening, sets of experiences that came to influence and shape the rest of my life. I had encountered so many admirable, good women who had been mistreated and harmed by the very men they had loved and trusted, and further persecuted by a society which judged them harshly. I hope that they came to find peace, and their nirvana in this world, or the next.

And what of Sean? In one of life's strangest of incidents, I discovered that he had sadly died, aged sixty years, predeceasing a second wife by five years, and leaving behind also, another nine children.

There, but for the Grace of God, go I.

ABOUT THE AUTHOR

The author lives in the Lake District in the UK with her long-standing partner, Kevin, and their animals. She has lived and worked in other parts of the country, namely: Manchester, London, Cheshire, Leicestershire, Gloucestershire, Wiltshire; and also in Kilkenny in the Republic of Ireland.

She has always had a great love of animals, and feels passionately about animal welfare issues. During her lifetime she has personally rescued many cats, dogs, and birds which have been neglected, abandoned, ill-treated, injured, and stray; and adopted others, all of whom became much loved pets, including many hens from the British Hen Welfare Trust which were hitherto reared and kept in cages by the egg industry, and thus unable to follow their natural instincts to forage and roam.

Susan is retired from a career in Education and Training, and now enjoys writing, engaging in the creative arts, collecting vintage finds, and visiting heritage museums.

She is writing her next memoir which, she says, is one of several more which she intends to write, having had, as she describes, 'many quite unusual, and profound experiences.'

She would like to thank all those who played a part in the making of this book: her partner, Kevin, and daughter Katy, for their love and support in encouraging her to write it; to Members of the Ulverston Writer's Group for their invaluable critiquing of her work; to Anne Hood, Poet and Writer of Wild Geese Poetry, who read her final manuscript in one fell swoop and not only discovered some errors but generously wrote a compelling review. A huge and grateful thank you, in particular, for the 'eagle eye' of Tom Lewis, who kindly and painstakingly read, and re-read the manuscript, and provided constructive comments and helpful suggestions; and last, but not least, an enormous thank you to Russell Holden from Pixel Tweaks, for his guidance in production, and his brilliant graphic design skills in transforming my lumpen caterpillar of a manuscript into a beautiful butterfly, about to take flight!

The author wishes to express her heartfelt gratitude and thanks to you all, for making this book possible.